PENGUIN  CLASSICS

The Complete Annotated Listing Spring 1999

The cover of the catalogue shows: (left) a detail of a Greek relief showing *Euterpe, Muse of Lyric Poetry* (photo: Ancient Art & Architecture); (right) a detail from *The Visit of the Country Relations* by Alexander Carse, by courtesy of the Duke of Buccleuch & Queensberry, KT.

PENGUIN CLASSICS

Penguin is the leading publisher of the classics in the English-speaking world. The Penguin Classics list was launched in 1946 and now includes over 800 titles from English and American literature, European, classical and non-Western literature in translation, philosophy and religion, history and politics, travel and art.

Penguin editions include comprehensive, critical introductions and textual notes provided by experienced scholars and editors, with additional features such as chronologies, further reading lists, glossaries and indexes.

Penguin Classics offer the widest range of authoritative and accessible editions of the world's greatest books.

PLEASE NOTE

Prices quoted are recommended retail prices
Prices and dates are provisional and subject to change
Prefix 6 digit isbn numbers in this catalogue with 0140 when ordering books

FOR FURTHER INFORMATION CONTACT

Penguin Press Marketing
*Penguin UK
27 Wrights Lane
London W8 5TZ

Fax 0171 416 3099

Visit Penguin Classics on the internet at: www.penguinclassics.com

🎧 – Available as a Penguin Audiobook

For a copy of the latest Penguin Audiobook catalogue
Please contact: Penguin Audiobook Department
at the Penguin UK address*

For more information about Penguin Music Classics
Please contact: Penguin General Marketing
at the Penguin UK address*
For sale in the UK and EIRE only

CONTENTS

ENGLISH LANGUAGE

LITERATURE

Courtesy of Viscount De L'Isle, from his private collection

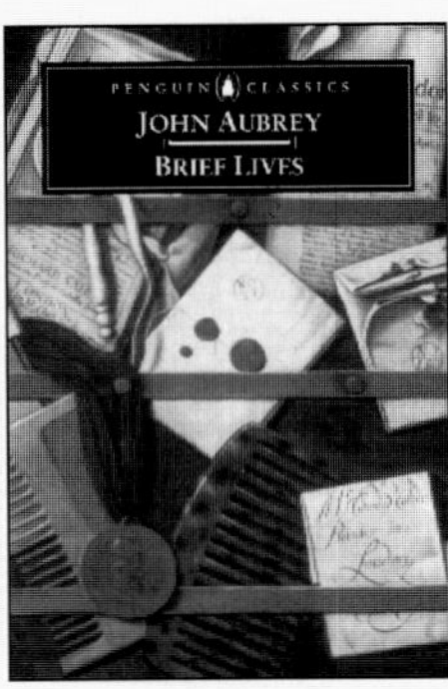

EDWIN A ABBOTT

1838–1926

FLATLAND: A ROMANCE OF MANY DIMENSIONS

Introduction by Alan Lightman

Narrated by A Square, *Flatland* is Edwin A Abbott's delightful mathematical fantasy about life in a two-dimensional world. Abbott's amiable narrator provides an overview of this fantastic world – its physics and metaphysics, its history, customs, and religious beliefs. But when a strange visitor mysteriously appears and transports the incredulous Flatlander to the Land of Three Dimensions, his worldview is forever shattered.

43531X 144pp £5.99

REISSUE FEBRUARY 99

JOHN AUBREY

1626–1697

BRIEF LIVES

Selected and edited with introduction by John Buchanan-Brown and a foreword by Michael Hunter

Although Aubrey's *Brief Lives* were ostensibly compiled as material for his friend Anthony Wood's histories of Oxford University and its alumni, they make an unforgettably vivid and revealing contribution to the oral history of Elizabethan and Stuart England.

435891 608pp £7.99

NEW MARCH 99

AUGUSTAN CRITICAL WRITING

Edited with an introduction by David Womersley

English literary criticism from 1660 to 1750 is collected in this engaging look back to a time before literary criticism had become codified and professionalized – when literary art, and readers' reactions to it, were considered not a separate sphere but an integral part of political, cultural and social life.

433732 496pp £10.99

JANE AUSTEN

1775–1817

The texts of Austen's novels in these new Penguin Editions are based on the first published editions and have been edited afresh. The editorial policy is one of minimum intervention with no attempt made to modernize spelling or punctuation to current practice. The results provide the reader with a lively and interesting text, as close to Austen's original as is possible.

EMMA 

Edited with an introduction by Fiona Stafford

Vital, interesting, complex and predisposed to play a power game with other people's emotions, Emma is one of Jane Austen's immortal creations. Her matchmaking, the consequent crisis, her bitter regrets and happy resolution are plotted with Austen's incomparable art in this sharp and sparkling comedy of self-deceit and self-discovery.

434151 448pp £2.50

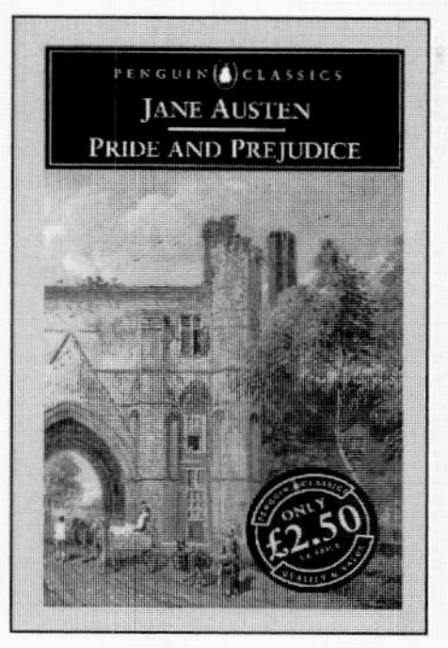

Lady Susan
The Watsons
Sanditon

Edited with an introduction by Margaret Drabble

These three works – one novel unpublished in her lifetime and two unfinished fragments – reveal Jane Austen's development as a great artist and throw light on the major novels as well as being enjoyable in their own right.

431020 224pp £2.50

Mansfield Park

Edited with an introduction by Kathryn Sutherland

Jane Austen draws on her cool irony and comic genius to full effect in this novel. The story of Fanny Price, her quiet, suffering heroine, the Crawfords, the Bertrams and their interlocking destinies, is played out with wit and profound psychological insight.

434143 480pp £2.50

Northanger Abbey

Edited with an introduction by Marilyn Butler

During an eventful social season at Bath, Catherine Morland is invited to Northanger Abbey, where she believes she has discovered all the trappings of the Gothic novels she so loves reading. As she learns to distinguish literature from life, Catherine must also confront the trials of imperiled love, true-life danger, and, especially, the inevitable necessity of learning to think for herself.

434135 288pp £2.50

Persuasion

Edited with an introduction by Gillian Beer

Jane Austen's last completed novel 'with its overwhelming sympathy with one person, Anne Elliot, is – despite its many scenes of social comedy and prudential realism – drenched in romance, a compensatory romance that rights a wrong beginning.' from the introduction

434674 272pp £2.50

NEW OCTOBER 98

Pride and Prejudice

Edited with an introduction by Vivien Jones

A delicious social comedy as well as a love story between the spirited Elizabeth Bennet and the aloof Mr Darcy, *Pride and Prejudice* is one of the most enduringly popular English novels.

434267 384pp £2.50

Sense and Sensibility

Edited with an introduction by Ros Ballaster

The first of Jane Austen's major novels, this has at its centre two strikingly different sisters: reserved, tactful and self-controlled Elinor and impulsively emotional and demonstrative Marianne. Austen goes beyond this simple antithesis to explore the tension that exists in every community between the needs of the individual and the demands of society.

434259 384pp £2.50

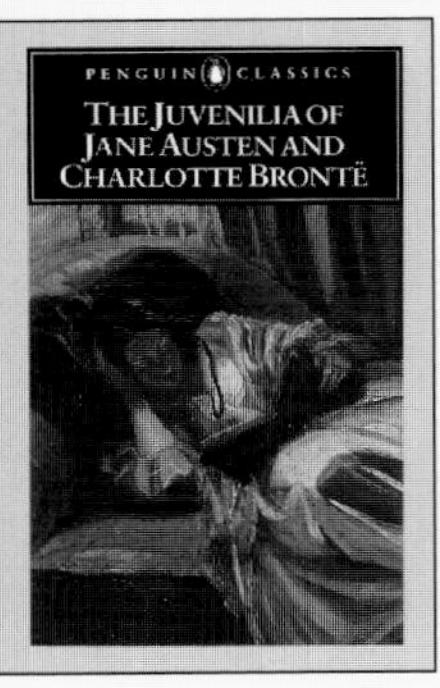

JANE AUSTEN AND CHARLOTTE BRONTË

Juvenilia of Jane Austen and Charlotte Brontë

Edited by Frances Beer

Both authors produced a considerable body of juvenilia, in which they experimented and developed character and style. Austen exhibits a merciless wit as she lampoons human vanities and vices, later sharpening into a maturer moral perspective, while Charlotte Brontë's romantic adventures display her concern for the psychological intricacies of her characters' relationships.

432671 400pp £5.99

FRANCIS BACON

1561–1626

The Essays

Edited with an introduction by John Pitcher

The genius of Francis Bacon is nowhere better revealed than in his essays. Whatever their subject, whether is it something as personal as 'Friendship' or as abstract as 'Truth', the essays combine a mixture of rhetoric and philosophy; and are perhaps the most complete and rounded examples of Bacon's literary style.

432167 288pp £8.99

WILLIAM BECKFORD

1759–1844

Vathek and Other Stories

Edited with an introduction by Malcolm Jack

An exuberant imagination and unrivalled scholarship are the hallmark of these oriental tales, satires and travel diaries. Malcolm Jack, in his introduction, explores Beckford's 'journeying spirit' and makes a stimulating reassessment of his reputation as a stylist and innovator.

435301 352pp £5.99

APHRA BEHN

1640–1689

Love-Letters between a Nobleman and His Sister

Edited with an introduction by Janet Todd

A witty, racy *roman à clef* in three volumes, set in the tumultuous years after the death of Charles II in 1685. A heady mix of eroticism, sex and politics, it concentrates on a sensational aristocratic scandal of the day, the seduction of Henrietta Berkeley by her sister's husband Lord Grey, a notorious libertine and rebel.

435379 512pp £6.99

Oroonoko, The Rover and Other Works

Edited with an introduction by Janet Todd

This selection demonstrates the full sophistication and vitality of Aphra Behn's genius. It contains two plays, together with *Love Letters to a Gentleman*, a choice of poems and two short novels *The Fair Jilt* and *Oroonoko* – which are among the most innovative prose writings of the seventeenth century.

433384 400pp £6.99

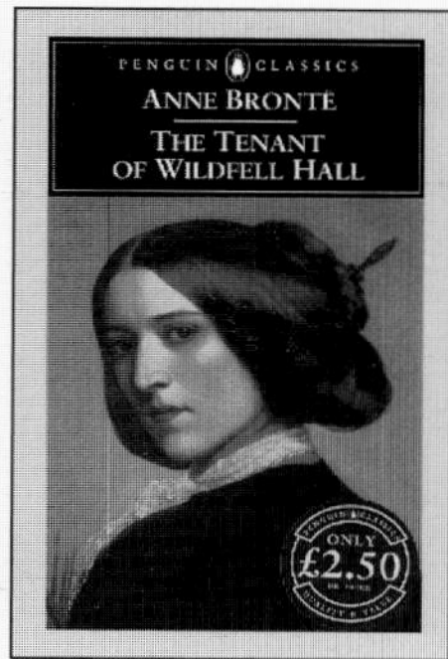

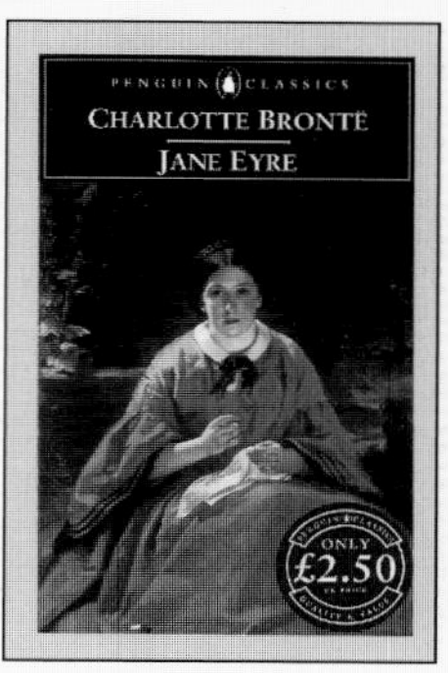

GEORGE BERKELEY

1685–1753

Principles of Human Knowledge Three Dialogues

Edited with an introduction by Roger Woolhouse

These two masterpieces of empirical thought, whether viewed as extreme scepticism or enlightened common sense, are a major influence on modern philosophy.

432930 224pp £6.99

MARY ELIZABETH BRADDON

1835–1915

Lady Audley's Secret

Edited by Jenny Bourne Taylor, with an introduction by Jenny Bourne Taylor with Russell Crofts

Weathering critical scorn, *Lady Audley's Secret* (1862) quickly established Mary Elizabeth Braddon as the leading light of Victorian 'sensation' fiction, sharing the honour only with Wilkie Collins. Addictive, cunningly plotted and certainly sensational, it draws on contemporary theories of insanity to probe mid-Victorian anxiety and the doubts that accompanied the rapid rise of consumer culture.

435840 512pp £7.99

ANNE BRONTË

1820–1849

Agnes Grey

Edited with an introduction by Angeline Goreau

Drawing on her own experiences, Anne Brontë wrote her first novel out of an urgent need to inform her contemporaries about the desperate position of unmarried, educated women driven to take up the only 'respectable' career open to them – that of a governess. Agnes's story is a compelling inside view of Victorian chauvinism and ruthless materialism.

432108 272pp £2.50

The Tenant of Wildfell Hall

Edited with an introduction by Stevie Davies

Helen Huntingdon is driven to leave her atrocious husband, abscond with her son and claim her right to an independant existence. This impassioned and bold treatment of the issue of women's equality shocked Victorian moralists and strikes the reader with its modernity today.

434747 576pp £2.50

CHARLOTTE BRONTË

1816–1855

Jane Eyre

Edited with an introduction by Michael Mason

How the orphaned Jane Eyre takes up the post of governess at Thornfield Hall, meets and loves Mr Rochester and discovers the impediment to their marriage, are elements in a story that transcends melodrama to portray a woman's passionate search for a wider and richer life than that traditionally accorded to her sex in Victorian society.

434003 576pp £2.50

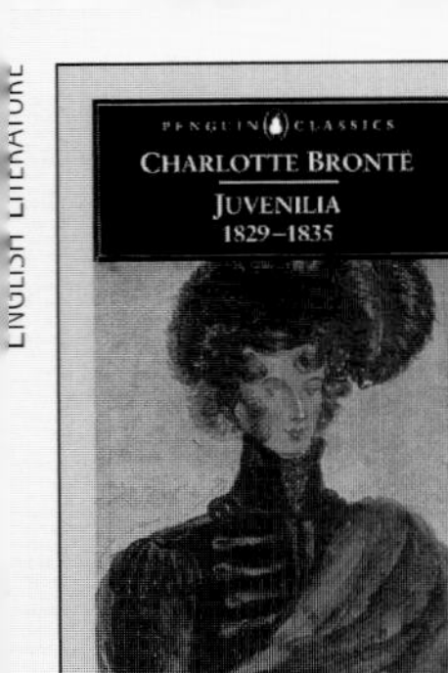

JUVENILIA 1829–1835

Selected, newly transcribed, and edited with an introduction by Juliet Barker

The delightful characters and lively imaginary worlds created by Charlotte Brontë together with her brother Branwell and her sisters are an essential key to the understanding of her mature novels. Charlotte herself referred to these childhood writings – stories, diary, papers and poems – written between 1829 and 1835, as a 'long apprenticeship in writing'.

435158 336pp £6.99

THE PROFESSOR

Edited with an introduction by Heather Glen

Published posthumously in 1857, Charlotte Brontë's first novel is a subtle portrayal of a self-made man and his use of power in an individualistic society that worships property and propriety.

433112 320pp £2.50

SHIRLEY

Edited by Andrew and Judith Hook

Set against the unrest of the Napoleonic wars, this novel follows two contrasting heroines and the men they love. Wider in scope than *Jane Eyre*, *Shirley* deals with social and political issues of the day.

430954 624pp £2.50

VILLETTE

Edited by Mark Lilly with an introduction by Tony Tanner

Charlotte Brontë's last novel is often regarded as her most emotionally and aesthetically satisfying work. It explores the nervous isolation, heroic fortitude and unrequited love of its narrator, Lucy Snowe.

431187 624pp £2.50

EMILY BRONTË

1818–1848

WUTHERING HEIGHTS

Edited with an introduction and notes by Pauline Nestor

The story of the passionate love between Catherine Earnshaw and the wild Heathcliff, told with wholly original emotional and imaginative power, has the depth and simplicity of an ancient tragedy.

434186 400pp £2.50

SIR THOMAS BROWNE

1605–1682

THE MAJOR WORKS

Edited with an introduction by C A Patrides

The brilliant author and physician, Sir Thomas Browne encapsulates seventeenth-century social, religious and intellectual concerns in his works *Religio Medici, Hydriotophia, The Garden of Cyprus, A Letter to a Friend* and *Christian Morals.*

431098 560pp £11.00

JOHN BUNYAN

1628–1688

GRACE ABOUNDING TO THE CHIEF OF SINNERS

Edited with an introduction by W R Owens

God and Satan are the chief protagonists in Bunyan's drama: they exist not as theological

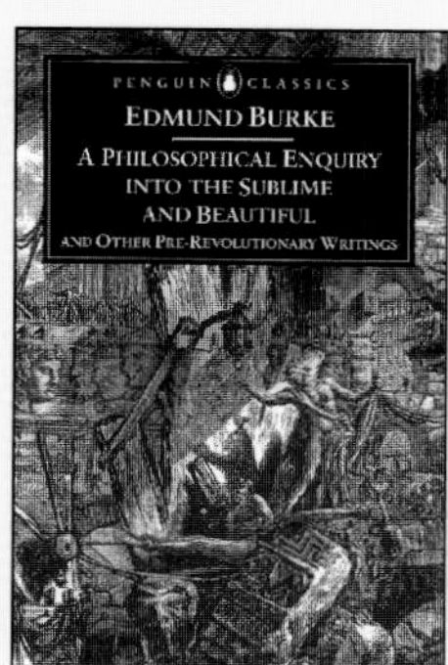

concepts but as terrifyingly immediate adversaries in the competition for Bunyan's soul. Written when he was imprisoned for his religious principles, this is a moving and inspiring account of his conversion.

432809 160pp £5.99

The Pilgrim's Progress

Edited with an introduction by
Roger Sharrock

The supreme classic of the English Puritan tradition, *The Pilgrim's Progress* follows Christian's pilgrimage through Vanity Fair, the Slough of Despond and Delectable Mountains towards the Celestial City. Rich and inventive, it had a profound effect on the English consciousness.

430040 336pp £2.50

EDMUND BURKE

1729–1797

A Philosophical Enquiry into the Sublime and Beautiful and Other Pre-Revolutionary Writings

Edited with an introduction by
David Womersley

A Vindication of Natural Society/ A Philosophical Enquiry into the Sublime and Beautiful/Thoughts on the Cause of the Present Discontents/Speech on American Taxation/ Speech on Conciliation with the Colonies/Letter to the Sheriffs of Bristol

Written when he was only twenty-eight, Burke's *Philosophical Enquiry* proved highly influential for later aesthetic thought.

436251 528pp £6.99

NEW NOVEMBER 98

Reflections on the Revolution in France

Edited with an introduction by
Conor Cruise O'Brien

The great debate on the French Revolution was sparked off by *Reflections*, which reveals Burke as a much more radical – even revolutionary – thinker than admitted by those who view him as the father of modern conservatism.

432043 400pp £6.99

FRANCES BURNEY

1752–1840

Evelina

Edited with an introduction by
Margaret Anne Doody

This epistolary portrait of female independence and the intrigues of the social classes introduced an entirely new form of novel – the comedy of manners – when it was published anonymously in 1778.

433473 560pp £6.99

SAMUEL BUTLER

1835–1902

Erewhon

Edited with an introduction by
Peter Mudford

Butler's tale of a traveller to a remote island, based on his experiences in New Zealand, combines the elements of traditional utopian fiction and the picaresque novel; the influence of *The Origin of the Species* on Butler's writing is apparent.

430571 272pp £5.99

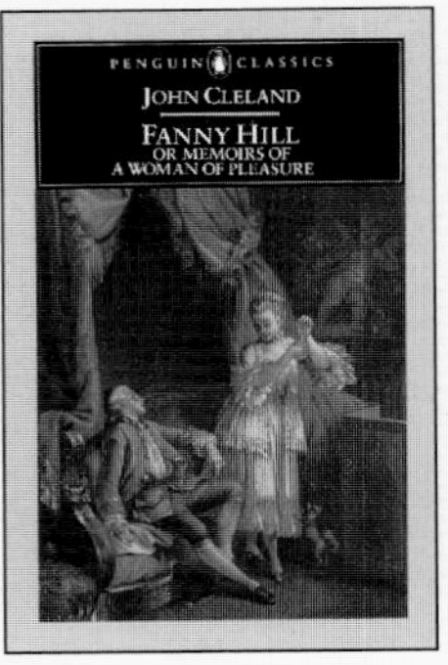

The Way of All Flesh

Edited by James Cochrane with an introduction by Richard Hoggart

A thinly disguised account of the author's own childhood and youth 'in the bosom of a Christian family'. With irony, wit and, sometimes, rancour, Butler savages the smug values and beliefs of the conventional Victorian family.

430121 448pp £5.99

THOMAS CARLYLE

1795–1881

Selected Writings

Edited with an introduction by Alan Shelston

An important and controversial figure in nineteenth-century thought, Carlyle was for Charles Dickens 'the man who knows everything'. This selection is intended to be representative of all stages of his influential career.

430652 400pp £9.99

LEWIS CARROLL

1832–1898

Alice's Adventures in Wonderland *and* Through the Looking Glass

Edited with an introduction and notes by Hugh Haughton. Illustrated by John Tenniel

Includes the two celebrated Alice stories together with Carroll's manuscript version, *Alice's Adventures Under Ground* – the 'germ' of *Alice's Adventures in Wonderland* – for the first time.

The most comprehensive annotated edition available.

433171 448pp £3.99

MARGARET CAVENDISH

1623–1673

The Blazing World and Other Writings

Edited with an introduction by Kate Lilley

These remarkable works of the flamboyant Duchess of Newcastle reveal not only a radical feminist, but a transgressor of every literary and sexual role and code. The title piece is the first work of science fiction ever written, depicting a utopia ruled by a warrior queen.

433724 272pp £7.99

JOHN CLELAND

1709–1789

Fanny Hill, or Memoirs of a Woman of Pleasure

Edited with an introduction by Peter Wagner

Described by James Boswell as 'a most licentious and inflaming book', modern readers appreciate *Fanny Hill* as a thoroughly entertaining and important work of erotic fiction, deserving a place in the history of the English novel.

432493 240pp £2.99

WILLIAM COBBETT

1763–1835

Rural Rides

Edited with an introduction by George Woodcock

Cobbett's *Rural Rides* is a travel book with several differences. Recording a number of fact-finding tours made on horseback through the south of England, it see-saws between evocative and accurate descriptions of the beauties

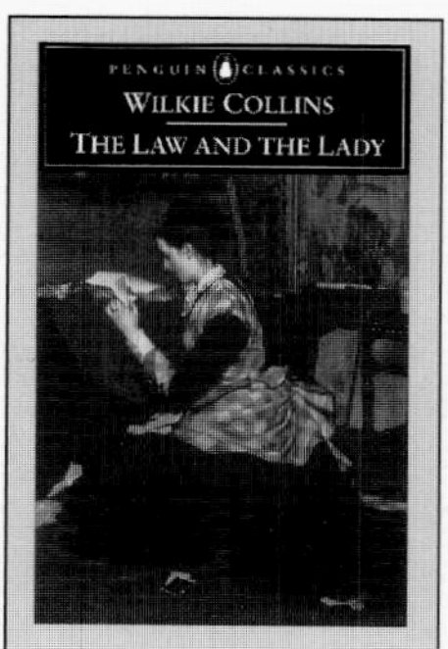

of the countryside, and indignant outbursts at the mushroom growth of cities and the sufferings of the exploited poor. For Cobbett saw the old rural England in its death struggle, and his book stands as a memorial to it.

430237 544pp £7.99

WILKIE COLLINS

1824–1889

Armadale

Edited with an introduction by John Sutherland

This intricately plotted Victorian melodrama draws on the substance and style of the popular press of the day: fraud, bigamy, drug addiction and domestic poisonings all make appearances as Collins chronicles the evil ways of a spectacularly beautiful but unscrupulous woman.

434119 752pp £3.99

The Law and the Lady

Edited with an introduction and notes by David Skilton

By the time *The Law and the Lady* appeared in 1875, *The Woman in White* and *The Moonstone* had already established Collins as the leading practitioner of 'sensation fiction'. *The Law and the Lady* builds on this tradition by introducing one of English literature's earliest woman detectives, Valeria Woodville, who investigates the murder of her husband's first wife, in the attempt to prove him guiltless.

436073 432pp £6.99

NEW SEPTEMBER 98

The Moonstone

Edited with an introduction by Sandra Kemp

The Moonstone, a priceless yellow diamond, is looted from an Indian temple and maliciously bequeathed to Rachel Verinder. On her eighteenth birthday, her friend and suitor Franklin Blake brings the gift to her. That very night, it is stolen again. No one is above suspicion, as the idiosyncratic Sergeant Cuff and Franklin piece together a puzzling series of events as mystifying as an opium dream and as deceptive as the nearby Shivering Sand.

434089 528pp £2.99

NEW NOVEMBER 98

No Name

Edited with an introduction by Mark Ford

Mercurial and unscrupulous, Magdalen Vanstone is Collins's most exhilarating heroine. The revelation of her illegitimacy and fall from social grace leads to a spirited quest to reclaim her identity.

43397X 640pp £3.99

The Woman in White 

Edited with an introduction by Julian Symons

The appearance of the woman in white begins what is still the greatest mystery thriller in the English language. The intricate plot and cast of carefully located characters combine in a story of confused identities whose surprises and dramatic compulsiveness make it impossible to put down.

430962 656pp £2.50

CHARLES DARWIN

1809–1882

The Origin of Species

Edited with an introduction by J W Burrow

The foundation of our current understanding about the place of humanity in the universe, this scientific account of Darwin's evolutionary view of the world challenged contemporary beliefs about Divine Providence and the fixity of species.

432051 480pp £5.99

The Voyage of the Beagle

Edited and abridged with an introduction by Janet Browne and Michael Neve

This shortened version of Darwin's journal of his five-year voyage on the HMS *Beagle* provides a profusion of detail about natural history and geology and illuminates the local people, politics and customs of the places he visited.

43268X 448pp £6.99

THOMAS DE QUINCEY

1785–1859

Confessions of an English Opium Eater

Edited with an introduction by Alethea Hayter

De Quincey's powerful evocation of his constant and bitter struggle against the incapacity and torpor of opium use brings to life the 'celestial' dreams and terrifying nightmares that transport and destroy the addict.

43061X 240pp £4.99

DANIEL DEFOE

1660–1731

A Journal of the Plague Year

Edited by Anthony Burgess and Christopher Bristow with an introduction by Anthony Burgess

The shocking immediacy of Daniel Defoe's description of a plague-racked city makes it one of the most convincing accounts of the Great Plague of 1665 ever written.

430156 256pp £4.99

Moll Flanders

Edited with an introduction by David Blewett

Born in Newgate prison and abandoned, Moll's life descends into adultery, bigamy, prostitution and theft. Apprehended and returned to Newgate, she finally undergoes a spiritual redemption.

433139 480pp £2.50

Robinson Crusoe 

Edited with an introduction by Angus Ross

The classic novel of a shipwrecked sailor on a desert island, *Robinson Crusoe* is also a moral tale and a puritan fable.

430075 320pp £2.50

Roxana

Edited by David Blewett

Defoe's last novel is a strange and tragic tale of the decline and defeat of a woman fatally tempted by the sinful glamour of immorality.

431497 416pp £5.99

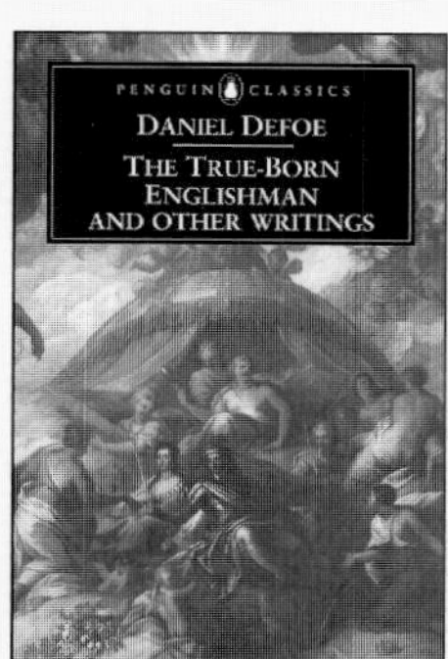

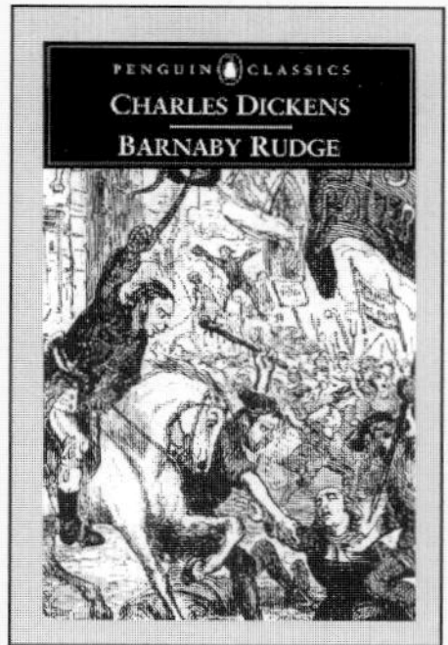

A TOUR THROUGH THE WHOLE ISLAND OF GREAT BRITAIN

Edited and abridged with an introduction by Pat Rogers

Defoe endows his guide to Britain just before the Industrial Revolution with a wild inventive streak that makes this book not only a classic of travel writing but a fascinating economic and social history.

430660 736pp £9.99

THE TRUE-BORN ENGLISHMAN AND OTHER WRITINGS

Edited with and introduction by P N Furbank and W R Owens

Long before the publication of *Robinson Crusoe*, Daniel Defoe had enjoyed a brief and dazzling career as a popular hero – and had established himself as one of the most vivid and powerful writers of his age. This collection brings together thirteen major pieces from the earlier, radical phase of Defoe's career, revealing him as an impassioned moralist, a superb stylist and a pioneering political journalist.

435727 336pp £8.99

CHARLES DICKENS

1812–1870

Based on the first volume editions of Dickens's novels, our new Penguin Classics have been comprehensively annotated and include the original illustrations.

AMERICAN NOTES FOR GENERAL CIRCULATION

Edited with an introduction by John S Whitley and Arnold Goldman

The youthful, still-rough United States of 1842 is vividly recalled in this journal of Dickens's famous tour, offering a fascinating view of the New World by one of the Old World's greatest writers and social thinkers.

430776 368pp £7.99

BARNABY RUDGE

Edited with an introduction by G W Spence

In this superb novel about individuals caught in the horrors of the rebellion of apprentices against their masters, Dickens dramatizes his fascination with private murder and public violence.

430903 768pp £4.99

BLEAK HOUSE

Edited with an introduction by Nicola Bradbury

Part romance, part melodrama, part detective story, this novel centres around the interminable land inheritance suit of Jarndyce and Jarndyce and spreads out among a web of relationships at every level of society from the simple-minded but self-important Sir Leicester Dedlock to Jo the street sweeper. Its story is a metaphor for the decay and corruption at the heart of British society.

434968 1088pp £3.99

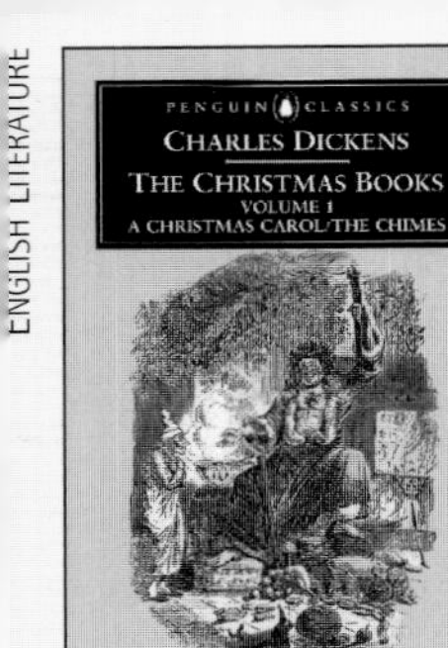

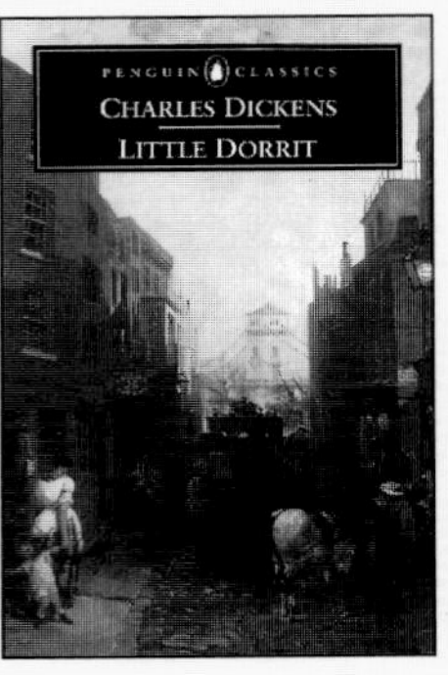

THE CHRISTMAS BOOKS VOLUME 1

Edited with an introduction by Michael Slater

A Christmas Carol, with its unique blend of comedy and horror and the delightful grotesque, Scrooge, continues to mark our celebrations of Christmas. *The Chimes* is a provocative satire of how the wealthy celebrate New Year's Eve.

430687 272pp £4.99

THE CHRISTMAS BOOKS VOLUME 2

Edited with an introduction by Michael Slater

The Cricket on the Hearth is a delightful comedy set in a world of toys; *The Battle of Life* and *The Haunted Man* share the theme of the morally beneficial effects of memory.

430695 368pp £4.99

DAVID COPPERFIELD

Edited with an introduction by Jeremy Tambling

Written in the form of an autobiography and intimately rooted in Dickens's own life, this is the evergreen story of a young man growing to maturity in both affairs of the world and affairs of the heart. Jeremy Tambling's provocative introduction delves into the novel's condemnation of repressive institutions – schools, prisons, and even the family – its pervasive, if subtle, acknowledgment of woman's sexuality, and its undertone of homoeroticism.

434941 960pp £3.99

DOMBEY AND SON

Edited by Peter Fairclough with an introduction by Raymond Williams

Against the teeming streets of mid-Victorian London, Dickens examines Britain's new industrial power and its potential for creation and destruction.

430482 992pp £5.99

GREAT EXPECTATIONS

Edited by Charlotte Mitchell with an introduction by David Trotter

With its rich array of characters and a narrative that moves from comedy to pathos to tragedy, *Great Expectations* is one of Dickens's most entertaining novels.

434895 544pp £2.50

HARD TIMES

Edited with an introduction by Kate Flint

With its vivid depiction of Coketown's tall chimneys trailing 'interminable serpents of smoke' and its evocations of the dismal conditions of oppressed workers, *Hard Times* is certainly an 'industrial novel'. While it conveys deep concern for children, family and home life, it is a heartfelt satire as well, targeting utilitarianism, self-help doctrines, and the mechanization of the mid-Victorian soul.

433988 368pp £2.50

LITTLE DORRIT

Edited with an introduction by Stephen Wall and notes and appendices by Helen Small

In *Little Dorrit* Dickens portrays a prison-world in which the shadow of the Marshalsea reaches from the rack-rented Bleeding Heart

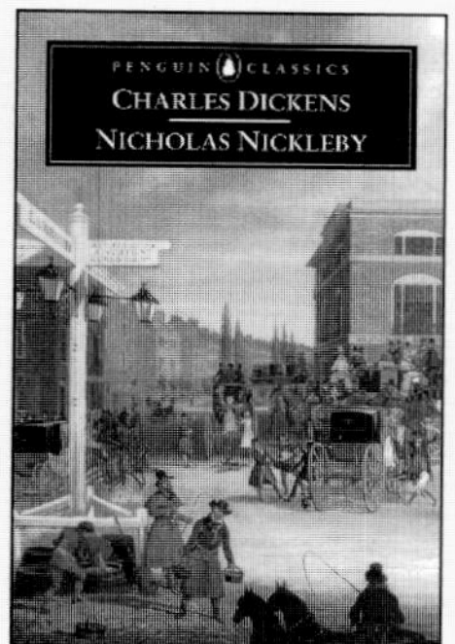

Yard to the high society of Harley Street and Hampton Court and the bureaucracy of the Circumlocution Office, as well as beyond the Alps to Venice and Rome.

434925 928pp £3.99

MARTIN CHUZZLEWIT

Edited with an introduction by P N Furbank

Moving from sunny farce to the grimmest reaches of criminal psychology, this study of selfishness and hypocrisy follows the lives of two brothers with very different fates.

430318 944pp £2.99

THE MYSTERY OF EDWIN DROOD

Edited by Arthur J Cox with an introduction by Angus Wilson

Unfinished at the time of Dickens's death, this novel explores the dark opium underworld and the uneasy and violent fantasies of its inhabitants.

43092X 320pp £3.99

NICHOLAS NICKLEBY

Edited with an introduction by Mark Ford

Nicholas Nickleby will always be one of the most exhilarating comic novels in English literature and one which G K Chesterton declared 'coincides with [Dickens's] resolution to be a great novelist'. Dickens created a great gallery of comic types whose treatment of his young hero serves to expose the social ills and horrors of the day.

435123 864pp £4.99

NEW MARCH 99

THE OLD CURIOSITY SHOP

Edited by Angus Easson with an introduction by Malcolm Andrews

This novel contains some of Dickens's most bizarre characters, including the lecherous dwarf Quilp, as well as his most sentimental creation, the innocent Little Nell, who is destroyed by an evil world.

43075X 720pp £3.99

OLIVER TWIST

Edited by Peter Fairclough with an introduction by Angus Wilson

This story of Oliver, a boy of unknown parentage who escapes a workhouse and embarks on a life of crime, shows how the lack of compassion in privileged society helps to make poverty a nursery of crime.

430172 496pp £2.50

OUR MUTUAL FRIEND

Edited with an introduction by Adrian Poole

In *Our Mutual Friend*, his last completed novel, Dickens turned again to question the life and soul of a society corrupted by money.

At the Boffin mansion, built on the fortune amassed from old Mr Harmon's dust heaps, and at the Veneering's superior dinner-table Dickens creates glorious comic satire. Beyond this, flowing through the city and the novel, the river Thames gives and promises death and renewal, dominating the landscape and the love stories of Bella Wilfer and Lizzie Hexam.

434976 928pp £4.99

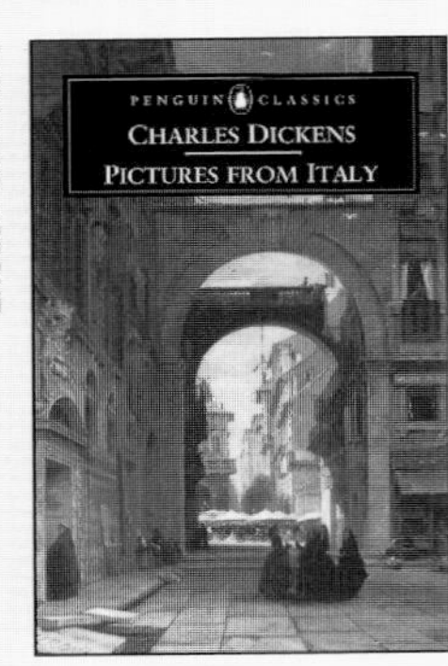

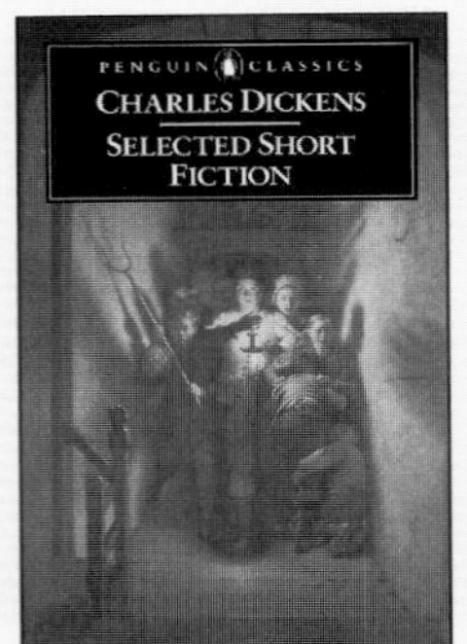

The Pickwick Papers

Edited with an introduction by Robert Patten

The story of the adventures of the charming, portly Sam Weller and his Pickwick Club catapulted the twenty-four-year-old Charles Dickens to fame.

430784 960pp £2.99

Pictures from Italy

Edited with an introduction by Kate Flint

A thrilling travelogue which is also deeply revealing about the author's anxieties and concerns, this neglected work deserves a secure place among the masterpieces of Dickens's maturity. He presents the country 'like a chaotic magic-lantern show, fascinated both by the spectacle it offers, and by himself as spectator ...' from the introduction

434313 272pp £7.99

Selected Journalism 1850–1870

Edited with an introduction by David Pascoe

'All who love Dickens have a strange sense that he is really inexhaustible.'

That was G K Chesterton's impression of Dickens's mature journalism and it still holds true. Dickens was always on the move, in his imagination and in the mile upon mile of nocturnal walks he made around London. He travelled, either literally or figuratively to prisons, theatres, slums, the Inns of Court, on journeys to the Continent and back to his childhood in Kent and London.

435808 672pp £9.99

Selected Short Fiction

Selections from *Sketches by Boz, The Uncommercial Traveller* and many other periodicals

Edited with an introduction by Deborah A Thomas

Divided into three sections – 'Tales of the Supernatural', 'Impressionistic Sketches', and 'Dramatic Monologues' – this volume reveals Dickens's recurring concerns and places them clearly in the context of related elements in his novels.

431039 432pp £6.99

Sketches by Boz

Edited with an introduction by Dennis Walder

Dickens's first book, published when he was twenty-four, *Sketches by Boz* is a wonderful miscellany of reportage, observation, fancy and fiction – all centring on the teeming metropolis of London. With its episodic structure, improvisational flourishes, comic invention, and cast of odd and eccentric characters, it introduces all the elements characteristic of Dickens's great novels.

433457 688pp £7.99

A Tale of Two Cities

Edited with an introduction by George Woodcock

In this stirring tale of the French Revolution, Dickens reveals much about his own 'psychological revolution', examining his own fears and innermost conflicts through the actions of Charles Darnay, Sydney Carton and Lucie Manette.

430547 416pp £2.50

BENJAMIN DISRAELI

1804–1881

Coningsby

Edited with an introduction by Thom Braun

Disraeli's finest work of fiction, *Coningsby* is full of wit, irreverence, intrigue and romance – set at the time of the 1832 Reform Act, a crossroads in nineteenth-century British social history.

431926 528pp £6.99

Sybil, or The Two Nations

Edited by Thom Braun with an introduction by R A Butler

Part of Disraeli's Young England trilogy, so vivid is this work's exposure of the gross inequalities of Victorian society that is has become one of the most important of British political novels.

431349 544pp £5.99

DIVINE RIGHT AND DEMOCRACY

An Anthology of Political Writing in Stuart England

Edited with an introduction by David Wootton

Reflecting the political debate that characterized England's century of revolution, these thirty-three thematically arranged selections prefigure modern conceptions of political rights and social change. The volume includes anonymous writers as well as James VI and James I, John Lilburne, Charles I, Richard Hooker, Roger Williams, Gerrard Winstanley, Frances Bacon, Algernon Sidney, John Locke, Bernard Mandeville and others.

432507 512pp £9.99

JOHN DONNE

1572–1631

Selected Prose

Edited with an introduction by Neil Rhodes

Reflecting the metaphysical clash between poetry and religion, John Donne's works explore the relationship between self and world, capturing the conflict between the spiritual and the secular. This volume includes 'Paradoxes', 'Problems', 'Biathanatos', 'Devotions upon Emergent Occasions', letters and sermons.

432396 352pp £7.99

GEORGE DU MAURIER

1834–1896

Trilby

Edited with an introduction by Daniel Pick

Set in the Latin Quarter of Paris, this novel is the story of Trilby, an artist's model who falls under the hypnotic spell of the cruel Svengali. He shapes her into a virtuoso singer, but in exchange her life becomes fatally tied to his.

434038 336pp £7.99

GEORGE ELIOT

1819–1880

Adam Bede

Edited with an introduction by Stephen Gill

The story of a beautiful country girl's seduction by a local squire and the bitter consequences is told with Eliot's peculiar, haunting power.

431217 608pp £2.99

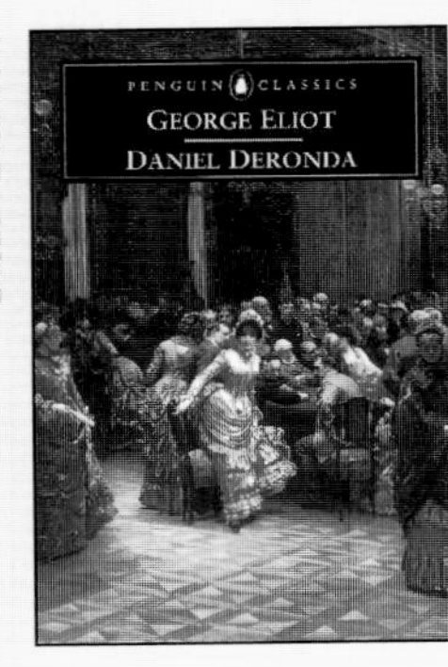

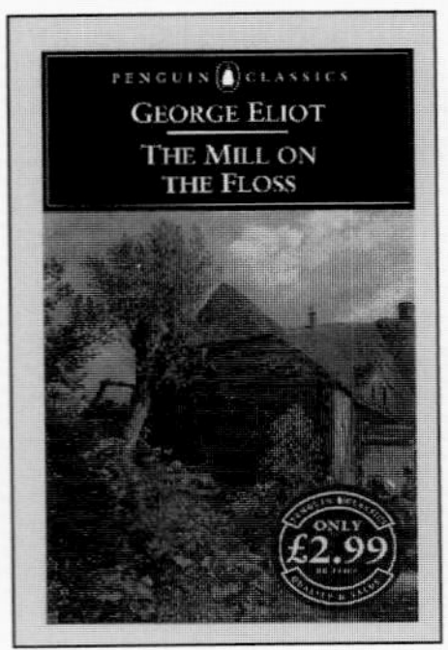

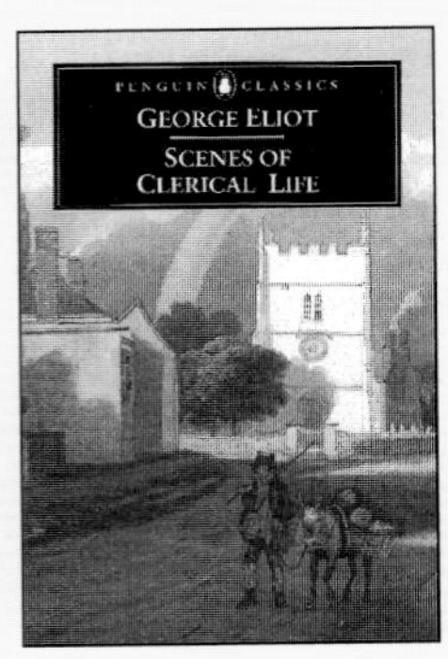

Daniel Deronda

Edited with an introduction by Terence Cave

In *Daniel Deronda*, her remarkable final novel, Eliot sets out to come to terms with the British Jews, a society-within-a-society of which her contemporaries seemed to be either oblivious or contemptuous. Eliot weaves the strands of her plot intimately, infusing them with her insights about human nature and daring the readers of *Middlemarch* and *Adam Bede* to consider realms of experience completely new to the Victorian novel.

434275 896pp £3.50

Felix Holt

Edited with an introduction by Lynda Mugglestone

Esther Lyon, the heroine, must choose between two men – one of independent wealth and one who is a political rascal – while also deciding her fate as a woman.

434356 592pp £4.99

Middlemarch

Edited with an introduction by Rosemary Ashton

This superb novel, Eliot's finest achievement, portrays the shape and texture of a rising provincial town of the 1830s through the remarkable story of determined heroine Dorothea Brooke – an idealist and a woman of conviction trapped in an agonising marriage to the egotistical Mr Casaubon.

433880 880pp £2.99

The Mill on the Floss

Edited with an introduction by A S Byatt

This affectionate and perceptive portrayal of childhood and adolescence in rural England features an imaginative heroine whose spirit closely resembles Eliot's own.

431209 704pp £2.99

Romola

Edited with an introduction by Dorothea Barrett

Published in 1863, *Romola* probes into the issues of gender and learning and of desire and scholarship.

434704 688pp £5.99

Scenes of Clerical Life

Edited with an introduction by Jennifer Gribble

Published at a time when religious issues were hotly debated, this collection of stories, including 'The Sad Fortunes of the Rev. Amos Barton', 'Mr. Gilfil's Love-Story', and 'Janet's Repentance', reflect Eliot's search for a religion of humanity that preserves the best in traditional Christianity.

436383 416pp £5.99

NEW JANUARY 99

Selected Essays, Poems and Other Writings

Edited by A S Byatt and Nicholas Warren with an introduction by A S Byatt

This collection of Eliot's shorter works includes contributions to the *Westminster Review*, selections from *Impressions of Theophrastus Such*, passages from her translations of

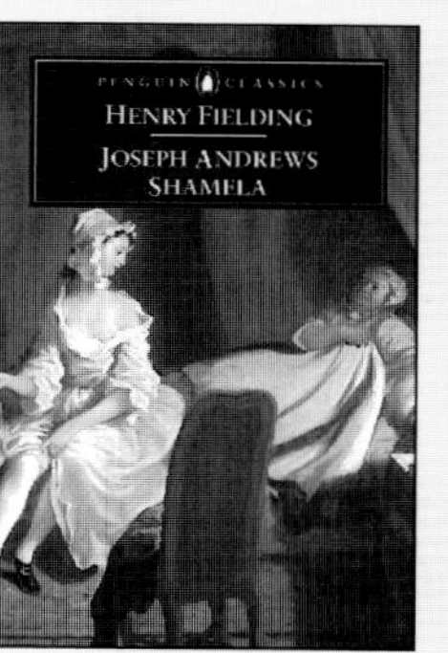

Feuerbach and Strauss, the 'Notes on Form in Art', and other major essays.
431489 544pp £8.99

SILAS MARNER

Edited with an introduction by David Carroll

In a novel that combines the emotional and moral satisfaction of a fairy tale with the realism and intelligence that are her hallmarks, Eliot counterpoints Silas's experiences with those of Godfrey Cass, the rich squire who is Eppie's father. Godfrey's refusal to claim Eppie, the offspring of his secret marriage to a woman far beneath him in social class, condemns him to a life filled with guilt and fear of disclosure.
434801 240pp £2.50

HENRY FIELDING

1707–1754

AMELIA

Edited with an introduction by David Blewett

A story of domestic and social disenchantment, Fielding's last novel represents a move away from the comic style of his earlier works toward a more subtle analysis of contemporary society's ills.
432299 608pp £6.99

JONATHAN WILD

Edited with an introduction by David Nokes

This edition includes Fielding's satiric novel – based on the life of a notorious thief – and Daniel Defoe's account of the real-life Jonathan Wild.
431519 288pp £5.99

JOSEPH ANDREWS

Edited with an introduction by R F Brissenden

One of the richest, sanest and funniest satires ever written, this story of a young man's determination to save his virtue features Parson Adams, one of the first great comic characters in British fiction.
431144 352pp £4.99

JOSEPH ANDREWS *AND* SHAMELA

Edited with an introduction by Judith Hawley

Shamela (1741) is a brilliant parody of Samuel Richardson's *Pamela*. Fielding's caricature of Richardson's heroine as a hypocritical prude who sets out to trick her master into marrying her is a burlesque masterpiece.

Joseph Andrews (1742), his first full-length novel, can also be seen as a response to Richardson, as the lascivious Lady Booby sets out to seduce her comically chaste servant Joseph.
433864 432pp £4.99
NEW MARCH 99

THE JOURNAL OF A VOYAGE TO LISBON

Edited with an introduction by Tom Keymer

When Fielding was winched aboard the *Queen of Portugal* bound for Lisbon in June 1754 he had small hope of surviving even the milder Portuguese winter. The author of *Joseph Andrews* and *Tom Jones* was 'dying from a complication of disorders' and the gravity of his illness sparks the unflinching humour and pathos of the *Journal*.
434879 192pp £6.99

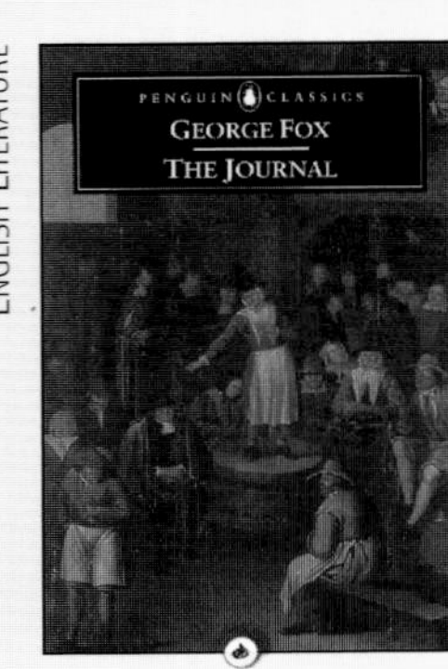

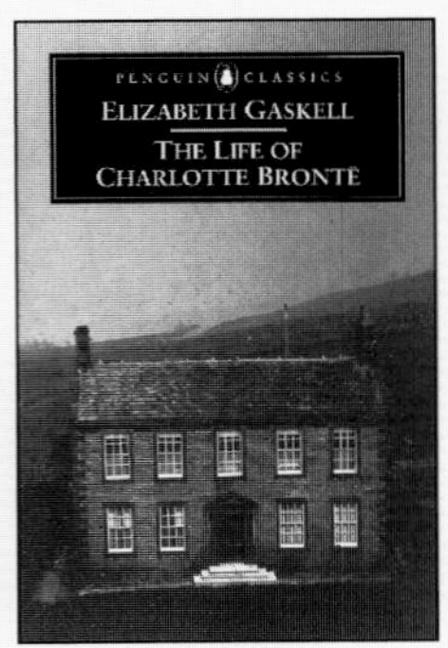

TOM JONES

Edited with an introduction by R P C Mutter

A novel rich in incident and coincidence, this picaresque tale of a lusty, handsome young man and his amorous adventures mocks the literary – and moral – conventions of Fielding's time.

430091 896pp £3.99

GEORGE FOX

1624–1691

THE JOURNAL

Edited by with an introduction by Nigel Smith

George Fox was the most famous of the early Quakers. His *Journal*, a remarkable account of his life's work, his often brutal persecution and his successes, was first published posthumously in 1694.

433996 576pp £7.99

NEW NOVEMBER 98

ELIZABETH GASKELL

1810–1865

CRANFORD *AND* COUSIN PHILLIS

Edited with an introduction by Peter Keating

Both *Cranford*, an affectionately ironic and understated depiction of an early Victorian country town, and *Cousin Phillis*, the story of an unfulfilled love affair, are concerned with the transition from old values to new.

431047 368pp £1.99

THE LIFE OF CHARLOTTE BRONTË

Edited with an introduction by Elisabeth Jay

Elizabeth Gaskell's *Life* appeared in 1857 to immediate popular acclaim among Victorian readers curious to discover more about the writer who had given *Jane Eyre* the subtitle, 'An Autobiography'. The resulting biography – the first full-length biography of a woman novelist by a woman novelist – almost single-handedly created the Brontë myth.

434933 544pp £5.99

MARY BARTON

Edited with an introduction by MacDonald Daly

A powerful depiction of industrial strife and class conflict in Manchester in the 1840s, Elizabeth Gaskell's first novel won widespread attention and established her reputation as a writer concerned with social and political issues.

43464X 464pp £2.50

NORTH AND SOUTH

Edited with an introduction by Patricia Ingham

Gaskell's great portrait of vastly differing conditions in England's industrial north and rural south explores the exploitation of the working class and links the plight of workers with that of women.

434240 480pp £2.50

RUTH

Edited with an introduction by Angus Easson

In *Ruth* Elizabeth Gaskell set out to portray, not 'the Condition of England' already famously addressed in *Mary Barton*, but the nature and sensibility of a fallen woman.

434305 448pp £5.99

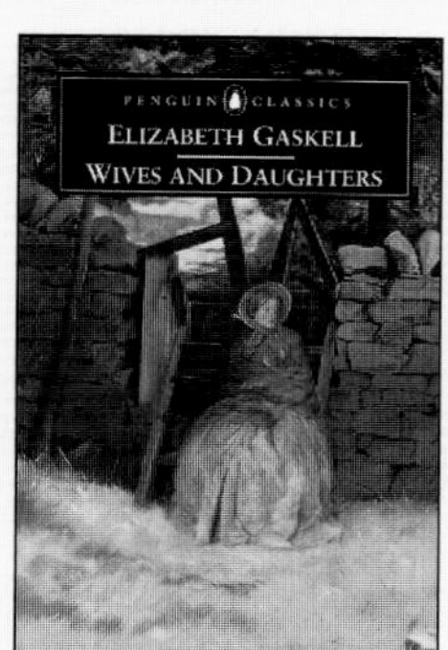

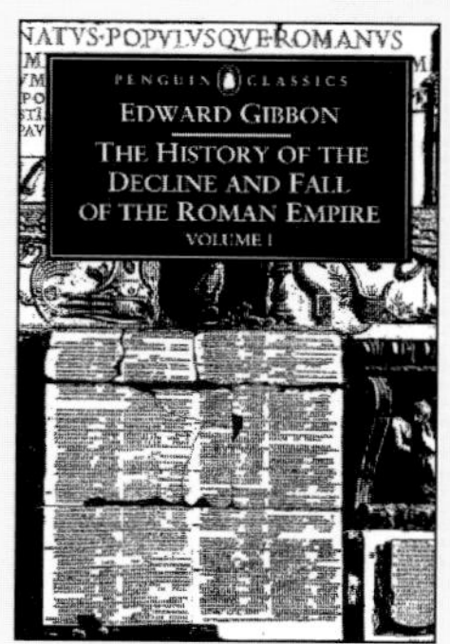

SYLVIA'S LOVERS

Edited with an introduction by Shirley Foster

Set against the tensions of the Napoleonic Wars, *Sylvia's Lovers* is a moving tale of a young woman caught between the attractions of two very different men. As Gaskell depicts Sylvia's fateful decision to marry one man while loving the other, she deftly interweaves the eternal flames of jealousy, unrequited love, and the consequences of individual choice.

434224 528pp £5.99

WIVES AND DAUGHTERS

Edited with an introduction by Pam Morris

This is Gaskell's comic tale of the coming-of-age of two very different stepsisters and of men and women constantly, if unintentionally, at cross-purposes. Beneath the nostalgic domesticity of *Wives and Daughters* readers will discover the same acute insights that have won Gaskell's earlier, more controversial novels new readership.

43478X 720pp £4.99

EDWARD GIBBON

1737–1794

THE HISTORY OF THE DECLINE AND FALL OF THE ROMAN EMPIRE

Edited with an introduction and appendices by David Womersley

'David Womersley's edition is an enormous achievement ... These volumes give us *The Decline and Fall of the Roman Empire* on a scale worthy of the original.' J G A Pocock, *London Review of Books*

This definitive three-volume edition presents a complete and unmodernized text, the author's own comments and notes, and his famous *Vindication*.

VOLUME 1

Launches the history by describing the Empire during the Age of Trajan and the Antonines.

433937 1232pp £15.00

VOLUME 2

Includes two of Gibbon's most subtle portraits, those of Constantine and Julian the Apostate.

433945 1024pp £15.00

VOLUME 3

Examines the enfeebled state of the Byzantine Empire and the spread of Islam.

433953 1360pp £15.00

THE DECLINE AND FALL OF THE ROMAN EMPIRE

Abridged

Edited with an introduction by Dero A Saunders and a preface by Charles Alexander Robinson Jr

The most celebrated historical work in the English language is condensed and combined with a summary of the deleted materials.

431896 704pp £7.99

MEMOIRS OF MY LIFE

Edited with an introduction by Betty Radice

The author of *The Decline and Fall of the Roman Empire* sheds light on some of his more renowned contemporaries and on eighteenth-century life in general in these fascinating memoirs.

432175 240pp £7.99

GEORGE GISSING
1857–1903

New Grub Street
Edited with an introduction by
Bernard Bergonzi

Through Edwin Reardon, a struggling novelist, and his friends on Grub Street – Milvain, a journalist, and Yule, an embittered critic – Gissing brings to life the literary climate of 1880s London.

430326 560pp £6.99

The Odd Woman
Introduction by Elaine Showalter

In its fierce criticism of a society that encouraged the oppression of women and consequently the arrogance and cruelty of men, *The Odd Woman* was astonishingly ahead of its time, and vividly reminds us that feminism is not a new concern.

433791 416pp £6.99

WILLIAM GODWIN
1756–1836

Caleb Williams
Edited with an introduction by
Maurice Hindle

A psychological detective novel about power, *Caleb Williams* was an imaginative contribution to the radical cause in the British debate on the French Revolution.

432566 448pp £7.99

An Enquiry Concerning Political Justice
Edited with an introduction by
Isaac Kramnick

The Enquiry, first published in 1793, established Godwin as the chief exponent of British radicalism – a tradition that calls for the establishment of rational anarchy to liberate the individual from the 'brute engine' of oppressive forms of government and the rule of law and order.

400303 832pp £11.00

OLIVER GOLDSMITH
1730–1774

The Vicar of Wakefield
Edited with an introduction by
Stephen Coote

This charming comedy is an artful send-up of the literary conventions of Goldsmith's time – the pastoral scene, the artificial romance, the stoic bravery of the hero – culminating in a highly improbable denouement.

431594 224pp £3.99

RICHARD HAKLUYT
1552–1616

Voyages and Discoveries
Edited and abridged with an introduction by
Jack Beeching

In this work of Hakluyt – a Renaissance diplomat, scholar and spy – lies the beginnings of geography, economics, ethnography and the modern world itself.

430733 448pp £8.99

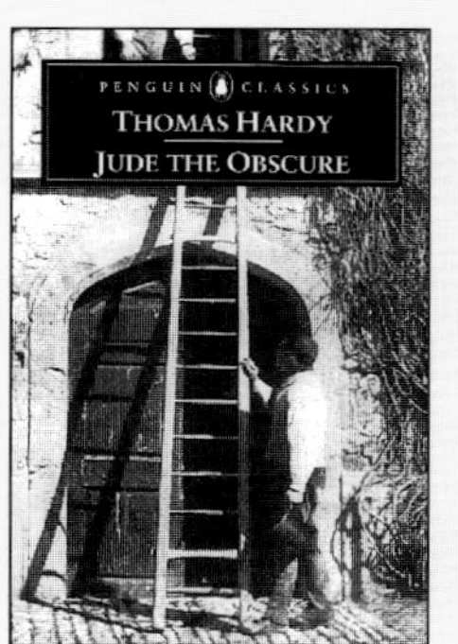

THOMAS HARDY

1840–1928

Returning to the first volume editions of Hardy's work, our new Penguin Classics present each novel as the creation of its own period without the revisions of later times.

DESPERATE REMEDIES

Edited with an introduction by Mary Rimmer

Blackmail, murder and romance are among the ingredients of Hardy's first published novel, which appeared anonymously in 1871. In its depiction of country life and insight into psychology and sexuality, it already bears the unmistakable imprint of Hardy's genius.

435239 512pp £6.99

THE DISTRACTED PREACHER AND OTHER TALES

Edited with an introduction by Susan Hill

Hardy captures the provincial experiences of his native Dorset and environs in eleven of his best and most representative stories, including 'The Withered Arm', 'Barbara of the House of Grebe', 'The Son's Veto', and 'A Tragedy of Two Ambitions'.

431241 368pp £2.99

FAR FROM THE MADDING CROWD

Edited by Ronald Blythe

Based on the author's firsthand knowledge of the attitudes, habits and idiosyncrasies of rural men and women, this is Hardy's best-loved and most humorous novel.

431268 496pp £2.99

THE HAND OF ETHELBERTA

Edited with an introduction by Tim Dolin

Hardy's London society comedy *The Hand of Ethelberta* is one of the most engaging and important of his early experiments in fiction. The brilliant adventuress Ethelberta is a butler's daughter who disguises her humble origins and launches a successful career as a society poet and public teller of stories. She brings her family to London and installs them incognito in her town house as servants, and happily exploits the attentions of four very different suitors in a plot rich in schemes and stratagems.

435026 512pp £6.99

JUDE THE OBSCURE

Edited with an introduction by Dennis Taylor

Jude The Obscure's fearless exploration of sexual and social relationships and its prophetic critique of marriage scandalized the late Victorian establishment and marked the end of Hardy's career as a novelist. He turned to poetry, after having created in Sue Bridehead an extraordinarily complex woman, his last heroine, an English Emma Bovary or Anna Karenin.

435387 528pp £2.50

A LAODICEAN

Edited with an introduction by John Schad

A Laodicean draws deeply on Hardy's personal experience: his early life as an architect, his frustration in love and his ambivalence about theology and the modern age.

435069 384pp £5.99

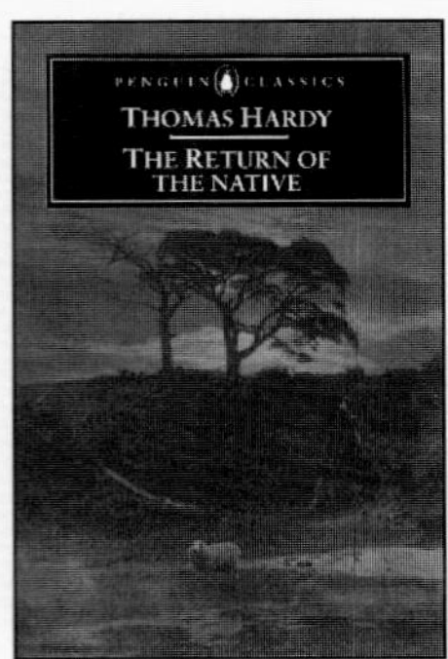

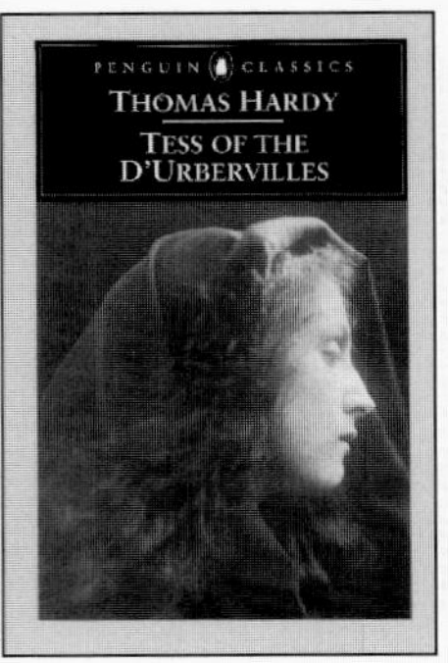

THE MAYOR OF CASTERBRIDGE

Edited with an introduction by Keith Wilson

Subtitled 'The Life and Death of a Man of Character', its focus is the spiritual and material career of Michael Henchard, whose governing inclinations are tragically at war with each other. A drunken impulse has lead him to sell his wife at a country fair; years later she and her daughter seek him out in Casterbridge, where he is now a rich and respected member of Wessex society. However, it is neither his family nor the ambitious manager of his corn business who bring him down but his own self-destructive nature.

435131 448pp £2.50

A PAIR OF BLUE EYES

Edited with an introduction by Pamela Daziel

In this compelling tale of love and deceit, Hardy depicts a society in which women are punished for their indiscretions rather than rewarded for their capacity to love.

435298 480pp £2.50

THE PURSUIT OF THE WELL-BELOVED *AND* THE WELL-BELOVED

Edited with an introduction by Patricia Ingham

In *The Pursuit of the Well-Beloved* and *The Well-Beloved*, Hardy writes two different versions of a strange story set in the weird landscape of Portland. The central figure is a man obsessed both with the search for his ideal woman and with sculpting the perfect figure of a naked Aphrodite. The pursuit finally fixes on three women called Avice Caro – grandmother, mother and daughter – in a way that mixes tragedy and high farce.

435190 416pp £4.99

THE RETURN OF THE NATIVE

Edited with notes by Tony Slade and an introduction by Penny Boumelha

The Return of the Native is a powerful novel of love, courtship and marriage centred on the beautiful and capricious heroine, Eustacia Vye. Hardy's passionate story tells of her relationships with Diggory Venn, Damon Wildeve and the returning 'native', Clym Yeobright, and reveals the disappointment of failed aspirations and the bitterness of class tensions.

435182 496pp £2.50

NEW MAY 99

THE RETURN OF THE NATIVE

Edited with an introduction by George Woodcock

431225 496pp £2.50

TESS OF THE D'URBERVILLES

Edited with notes by Tim Dolin and an introduction by Margaret Higonnet

Tess of the D'Urbervilles is one of the most moving and poetic of Hardy's novels, largely because it expresses the cruel workings of fate on its beautiful, tragic heroine. Hardy's harshest criticism is reserved for social hypocrisy and the lack of understanding that condemns Tess to her fate; but his critics did not necessarily agree with his assessment of his heroine as 'A Pure Woman' as Hardy subtitled his novel.

43514X 592pp £2.99

NEW JULY 98

The Trumpet-Major

Edited with an introduction by
Linda M Shires

The Trumpet-Major, set against the background of the Napoleonic wars, is a fascinating story of love and desire. Lyrical and light-hearted in tone, yet shot through with Hardy's characteristic irony, it is one of his most underrated and unpredictable works.

435409 416pp £2.99

Under the Greenwood Tree

Edited with an introduction by Tim Dolin

Under the Greenwood Tree appears to be pastoral romance at its most sunlit and good-humoured, and has been called the 'most nearly flawless of Hardy's novels'. For the author, who drew out the associations with this own childhood in later revisions, the novel came to epitomize a past that had been forever lost to him and to England.

435530 288pp £2.50

The Withered Arm and Other Stories

Edited with an introduction by Kristin Brady

Several of the stories in *The Withered Arm* were collected to form the famous volume, *Wessex Tales* (1888), the first time Hardy denoted 'Wessex' to describe his fictional world. This is the first of a new two-volume selection of Hardy's short stories.

435328 464pp £5.99

NEW MARCH 99

The Woodlanders

Edited with an introduction by
Patricia Ingham

Thomas Hardy said of *The Woodlanders* that he liked it 'as a story' the best of all his novels. In it, he explores the implications of evolution, the role of social class and the nature of women.

435476 464pp £2.50

WILLIAM HAZLITT

1778–1830

Selected Writings

Edited with an introduction by
Ronald Blythe

Writings by the prolific eighteenth-century journalist and essayist Hazlitt are alive with his cantankerous, uncompromising spirit and his radical protests.

430504 512pp £7.99

THOMAS HOBBES

1588–1679

Leviathan

Edited with an introduction by
C B MacPherson

Written amid the turmoil of the English civil war, Hobbes's apologia for the emergent seventeenth-century mercantile society speaks directly to twentieth-century minds in its concern for peace, systematic analysis of power, and elevation of politics to the status of a science.

431950 736pp £6.99

DAVID HUME

1711–1776

Dialogues Concerning Natural Religion

Edited with an introduction by Martin Bell

Modelled on Cicero's *De natura deorum*, this classic treatise on natural religion portrays the eighteenth-century conflict between scientific theism and philosophical skepticism. Hume savages the traditional arguments for the existence of God and suggests that the only religion that can stand up to serious scrutiny is one that is rationally and philosophically derived by the human mind.

445366 160pp £6.99

A Treatise of Human Nature

Edited with an introduction by Ernest C Mossner

The first work of this influential philosopher is an unprecedented extension of the Copernican revolution in science to the realm of philosophy.

432442 688pp £8.99

ELIZABETH INCHBALD

1753–1821

A Simple Story

Edited with an introduction by Pamela Clemit

The author's avowed purpose in this tale is to show the value 'of a proper education'. She describes the disastrous marriage of Miss Milner, a gay and empty-headed flirt, to Lord Elmwood, formerly a priest and her guardian, and the effects of her behaviour on their daughter Matilda.

434739 368pp £6.99

SAMUEL JOHNSON

1709–1784

History of Rasselas, Prince of Abissinia

Edited with an introduction by D J Enright

The pilgrimage of Rasselas from Abissinia to Egypt is used as a vehicle for Johnson's musings on such wide-ranging subjects as flying machines, poetry, marriage and madness.

43108X 160pp £3.99

Selected Writings

Edited with an introduction by Patrick Crutwell

Generous selections from Johnson's major works include 'A Journey to the Western Islands of Scotland', 'The Dictionary of the English Language', and 'The Lives of the English Poets', as well as portions of his journals, letters and papers.

430334 576pp £10.99

MATTHEW LEWIS

1775–1818

The Monk

Edited with an introduction by Christopher MacLachlan

This masterpiece of Gothic fiction combines sheer sensationalism with a powerful expression of Lewis's deepest anxieties and most taboo feelings about women and sex. Savaged by critics for its blasphemy and obscenity, particularly since the author was a Member of Parliament, it soon attracted thousands of readers keen to see if it lived up to its lurid reputation.

436030 416pp £6.99
NEW OCTOBER 98

JOHN LOCKE

1632–1704

An Essay Concerning Human Understanding

Edited with an introduction and notes by Roger Woolhouse

In *An Essay Concerning Human Understanding* (1690), Locke provides a complete account of how we acquire everyday, mathematical, natural scientific, religious and ethical knowledge. Rejecting all appeals to authority and the theory that some knowledge is innate in us, Locke argues that it derives from sense perceptions and experience, as analysed and developed by reason.

434828 832pp £9.99

Political Writings

Edited with an introduction by David Wootton

This comprehensive selection brings together the main published works (including *The Second Treatise of Government* – a key founding liberal text) as well as letters to friends, a report on poor relief and even material from private papers. The result is the first fully-rounded picture of Locke's political thought.

433104 496pp £7.99

CHARLES LYELL

1797–1875

Principles of Geology

Edited with an introduction by James A Secord

Charles Lyell's *Principles of Geology* profoundly influenced Darwin as he voyaged on the Beagle and developed the theory of natural selection. A hugely ambitious attempt to forge links between observable causes – volcanoes, earthquakes, rivers, tides and storms – and the current state of the earth, the *Principles* proved crucial in the long-running dispute between science and scripture.

43528X 528pp £9.99

LORD MACAULAY

1800–1859

The History of England

Edited and abridged with an introduction by Hugh Trevor-Roper

Macaulay's monumental *History* covers the period from the accession of James II through the 1688 revolution and up to the death of William III in 1702.

431330 576pp £9.99

THOMAS MALTHUS

1766–1834

An Essay on the Principle of Population

Edited with an introduction by Antony Flew

In a thesis that explores the disparity between the potential rates of population growth and the means of subsistence, Malthus presents the ultimate demographic choice: starvation or restraint.

43206X 304pp £7.99

BERNARD MANDEVILLE

1670–1773

THE FABLE OF THE BEES

Edited with an introduction by Philip Harth

This masterpiece of eighteenth-century British satire sparked great social controversy by rejecting a positive view of human nature and arguing the necessity of vice as the foundation of an emerging capitalist economy.

445412 416pp £8.99

SIR JOHN MANDEVILLE

c. 1350

THE TRAVELS OF SIR JOHN MANDEVILLE

Translated with an introduction by
Charles W R D Moseley

Though it is still disputed if, and how far, Mandeville actually travelled, his travelogue was consulted for hard geographical information by Leonardo da Vinci and Columbus and stands today as an informative portrait of fourteenth-century Europe.

444351 208pp £7.99

DELARIVIER MANLEY

1663–1724

THE NEW ATALANTIS

Edited with an introduction by Ros Ballaster

Writer and wit, proto-feminist and political intriguer, Delarivier Manley shared equal notoriety as a satirist with her friend Jonathan Swift, and *New Atalantis* is her major work.

The book tells of Astrea, Goddess of Justice borne by the winds to Atalantis, where she meets her long-lost mother Virtue and is guided round the island by Lady Intelligence. Laced with autobiography, and political and erotic scandal, it was designed to expose the 'secret lives' of the rich and powerful in Stuart England and, not surprisingly, was suppressed on publication in 1709.

433708 336pp £8.99

HENRY MAYHEW

1812–1887

LONDON LABOUR AND THE LONDON POOR

Selected and with an introduction by
Victor E Neuburg

London Labour and the London Poor originated in a series of articles written for the *Morning Chronicle* in 1849–50, when Mayhew was at the height of his powers as a journalist, and was eventually published in four volumes in 1861–2. Victor Newburg's judicious selection ranges from costermongers to ex-convicts, from chimney-sweeps to vagrants, and includes illustrations from the 1865 impression. The underprivileged of London become extraordinarily alive – and Dickens is shown to be no exaggerator of life on the breadline in the middle of the nineteenth century.

432418 544pp £9.99

GEORGE MEREDITH

1828–1909

THE EGOIST

Edited with an introduction by
George Woodcock

In this consummate portrait of vanity and egoism, Meredith uses comedy as the great dissolver of artifice.

430342 608pp £7.99

The Ordeal of Richard Feveral

Edited with an introduction by Edward Mendelson

The war between the sexes and the generations, myths of Eden and Utopia, and the psychology of sexual jealousy and repression are explored by Meredith in this, his wonderfully ironic and impassioned first novel. *The Ordeal of Richard Feverel* concerns Sir Austin Feverel's misconceived attempts to educate his son Richard according to a system of his own devising.

434836 560pp £7.99

NEW OCTOBER 98

JOHN STUART MILL

1806–1873

Autobiography

Edited with an introduction by John Robson

This 1873 work by the founder of Britain's Utilitarian Society and the author of *System of Logic* and *Principles of Political Economy* describes Mill's intellectual and moral development from his earliest years to maturity.

433163 240pp £6.99

On Liberty

Edited with an introduction by Gertrude Himmelfarb

Dedicated to the principle of the personal sovereignty of the individual, Mill's most famous work still stands as an essential treatise on the subject of human liberty.

432078 192pp £1.99

Principles of Political Economy

Edited with an introduction by Donald Winch

This volume contains the two concluding books of Mill's durable classic – *Influence of the Progress of Society on Production and Distribution* and *On the Influence of Government* – as well as important passages regarding socialism and the distribution of property.

432604 400pp £7.99

JOHN STUART MILL AND JEREMY BENTHAM

1748–1832

Utilitarianism and Other Essays

Edited with an introduction by Alan Ryan

Bentham's and Mill's influential socio-political ideas are set forth in essays and selections from larger works, enhanced by Alan Ryan's extensive introduction analysing the origins, development and historical context of these ideas.

432728 352pp £6.99

LADY MARY WORTLEY MONTAGU

1689–1762

Selected Letters

Edited with an introduction by Isobel Grundy

Whether describing the Turkish baths in Sofia or the London social scene, negotiating her marriage settlement or declaring her passion for a young Italian, Lady Mary Wortley Montagu wrote some of the liveliest letters in the English language.

434909 576p £9.99

THOMAS MORE
1477–1535

Utopia
Translated with an introduction by Paul Turner

Utopia revolutionized Plato's classic blueprint for the perfect republic – later seen as a source of Anabaptism, Mormonism, and even Communism.

441654 160pp £4.99

WILLIAM MORRIS
1834–1896

News from Nowhere and Other Writings
Edited with an introduction by Clive Wilmer

Contained within one volume are the brilliant utopian novel *News from Nowhere* (1891) and essays by the socialist, pioneering environmentalist, designer-craftsman William Morris, whose antipathy toward the dehumanization of the Industrial Revolution was well known.

433309 480pp £7.99

THOMAS NASHE
1567–1601

The Unfortunate Traveller and Other Works
Edited with an introduction by J B Steane

Elizabethan manners, morality and mirth are captured in this selection from the works of Thomas Nashe – pamphleteer, poet, satirist, scholar, moralist and jester.

430679 512pp £9.99

JOHN HENRY NEWMAN
1801–1890

Apologia Pro Vita Sua
Edited with an introduction by Ian Ker

This spiritual autobiography of great power was written in response to personal attacks and conceived as a justification of his own actions when Newman's conversion to Roman Catholicism rocked the Church of England and escalated the spread of anti-Catholicism in Victorian England.

433740 608pp £8.99

THOMAS PAINE
1737–1809

Common Sense
Edited with an introduction by Isaac Kramnick

Published anonymously in 1776, *Common Sense* was instrumental in initiating the movement that established the independence of the United States. Drawn from Paine's experience of revolutionary politics, this treatise formulates the principles of fundamental human rights later expounded in his *Rights of Man*.

390162 128pp £5.99

Rights of Man
Edited with an introduction by Eric Foner and notes by Henry Collins

Written in reply to Burke's *Reflections on the Revolution in France*, Paine's *Rights of Man* enshrines the radical democratic attitude in its purest form.

390154 288pp £5.99

Thomas Paine Reader

Edited with an introduction by Michael Foot and Isaac Kramnick

This collection focuses on Paine as the political theorist who was an inspiration to Americans in their struggle for independence and the most incendiary of radical writers.

444963 544pp £8.99

WALTER PATER

1839–1894

Marius the Epicurean

Edited with an introduction by Michael Levey

This inimitable historical and autobiographical fiction, set in the Rome of Marcus Aurelius, reflects the values of late-Victorian England.

432361 320pp £8.99

THOMAS LOVE PEACOCK

1785–1866

Nightmare Abbey/Crotchet Castle

Edited with an introduction by Raymond Wright

Two of Peacock's wittiest works, parodies of the Gothic novel's excesses, are included here in one volume.

430458 288pp £6.99

SAMUEL PEPYS

1633–1703

The Shorter Pepys

Selected and edited by Robert Latham

Unequalled for its frankness, high spirits and sharp observations, Pepys's diary is both a marvellous slice of seventeenth-century life and an acknowledged literary masterpiece. Containing about a third of the original text, this skilfully compressed *Shorter Pepys* is ideally adapted to the needs of a modern audience.

433767 1152pp £14.99

SIR JOSHUA REYNOLDS

1723–1792

Discourses

Edited with an introduction by Pat Rogers

The art criticism and philosophical essays of Sir Joshua Reynolds, England's masterful portrait painter and literary stylist, were first presented to the students of the Royal Academy after he became its first president in 1768.

432787 432pp £8.99

SAMUEL RICHARDSON

1689–1761

Clarissa

Edited with an introduction by Angus Ross

This tale of attracted lovers – one a virtuous young woman, the other a charming and wicked young man – is, like *Pamela*, a novel told in psychologically revealing letters.

432159 1536pp £20.00

Pamela

Edited by Peter Sabor with an introduction by Margaret A Doody

Told in a series of letters, this story of a maid pursued by her dead mistress's son features the first British heroine to work for a living and deals with such matters as the perversion of sex into power, a radical theme in 1740.

431403 544pp £5.99

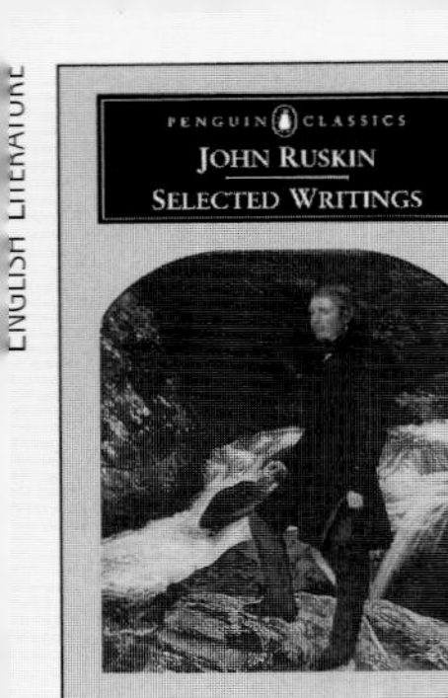

THE ROMANTICS ON SHAKESPEARE

Edited with an introduction by Jonathan Bate

In the decade 1808–18 three men, Schlegel, Coleridge and Hazlitt, produced some of the finest criticism on Shakespeare ever written. This anthology brings as well as substantial selections from their work, together with contributions from other contemporary giants of European literature, including Goethe, Stendhal, Hugo and Keats. Jonathan Bate has arranged the anthology so that general discussion is followed by readings of individual plays, and he provides an excellent introduction.

436480 592pp £9.99

JOHN RUSKIN

1819–1900

SELECTED WRITINGS

Selected and edited with an introduction by Kenneth Clark

Writing on art, literature, politics, nature and his own character convey the range of Ruskin's intellect and the tenor of his era.

433554 384pp £8.99

UNTO THIS LAST AND OTHER WRITINGS

Edited with an introduction and commentary by Clive Wilmer

The complete text of *Unto This Last*, Ruskin's influential critique of the science of political economy and the doctrine of unhindered industrialization, is presented with selections from *Modern Painters*, *The Stones of Venice*, and *Fors Clavigera*.

432116 368pp £9.99

MARY SHELLEY

1797–1851

FRANKENSTEIN

Edited with an introduction by Maurice Hindle

Shelley's Gothic horror tale, written when she was nineteen for her husband and their friend Lord Byron, was an immediate bestseller in 1818. This definitive new edition contains the revised, original text.

433627 320pp £2.50

MARY WOLLSTONECRAFT AND MARY SHELLEY

MARY/MARIA/MATILDA

Edited with an introduction by Janet Todd

Three short novels written by mother and daughter offer insight into the personal lives of both authors as they illuminate struggles for identity within the early feminist movement.

433716 256pp £6.99

SIR PHILIP SIDNEY

1554–1586

ARCADIA

Edited with an introduction by Maurice Evans

As much a work of entertainment and wit as of instruction, *Arcadia* affords the best insight we have into the tastes and standards of the Elizabethans and embodies the highest literary aspirations of the age.

43111X 880pp £11.00

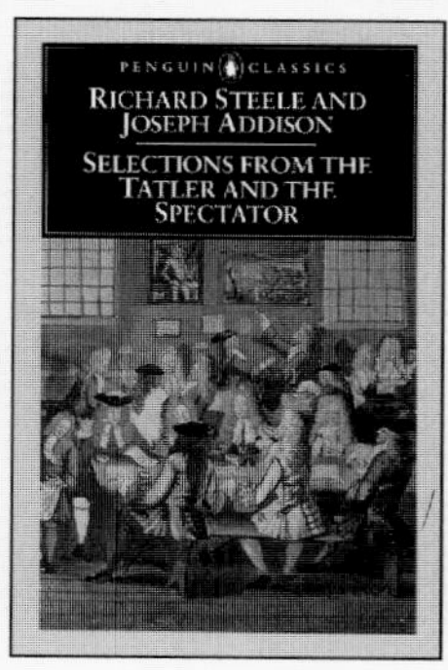

TOBIAS SMOLLETT

1721–1771

The Expedition of Humphry Clinker

Edited with an introduction by Angus Ross

Written towards the end of Smollett's life, this picaresque tour of eighteenth-century British society abounds with eccentric characters and comic adventures.

430210 416pp £4.99

Roderick Random

Edited with an introduction by David Blewett

Narrated by a decidedly unheroic hero, *Roderick Random* is a picaresque novel nonpareil, filled with rough humour, unlikely coincidences, and hilariously indiscreet comments on society. Smollett drew on his own life, incorporating elements from his impoverished youth, his work as a naval surgeon, his sojourn in the West Indies, and his encounters with London society.

433325 512pp £6.99

RICHARD STEELE AND JOSEPH ADDISON

Selections from the *Tatler* and the *Spectator*

Edited with an introduction and notes by Angus Ross

A selection of essays from two major periodicals that played a significant part in the shaping of English – and indeed European – culture during the eighteenth century.

The *Tatler*, first published in 1709, and the *Spectator*, which succeeded it in 1712, were the work of two formidable editors, Richard Steele and Joseph Addison. Arranged under such subjects as *Men, Women and Manners*, *Politics and Public Affairs* and *Essays in Criticism*, this selection of essays gives some of the flavour of the social, political and literary life of London in the reign of Queen Anne.

432981 592pp £8.99

LAURENCE STERNE

1713–1768

The Life and Opinions of Tristram Shandy, Gentleman

Edited by Melvyn New and Joan New, with an introductory essay by Christopher Ricks and an introduction and notes by Melvyn New

'Nothing odd will do long,' said Dr Johnson; '*Tristram Shandy* did not last.'

But Tristram Shandy has lasted, to be cherished in the century of Joyce, Rushdie and Fuentes perhaps even more than in the eighteenth. No one description will fit this strange, eccentric, endlessly complex masterpiece. It is a fiction about fiction-writing in which the world is as much infused with wit and genius as the theme of inventing it. It is a joyful celebration of the infinite possibilities of the art of fiction, and a wry demonstration of its limitations.

435050 720pp £2.99

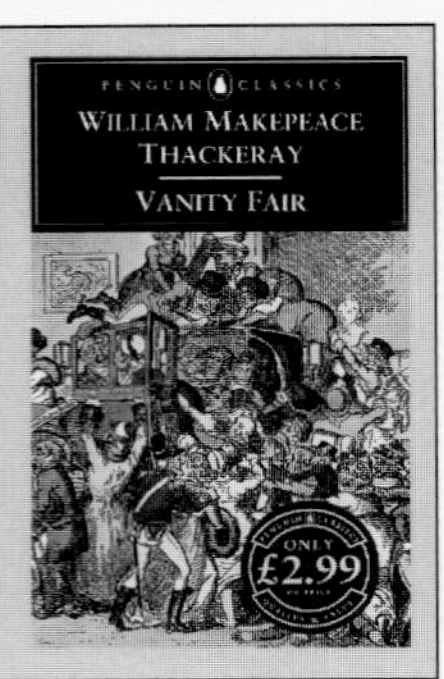

A Sentimental Journey Through France and Italy

Edited by Graham Petrie with an introduction by A Alvarez

Begun as an account of a trip through France and Italy, this novel is a treasury of dramatic sketches, ironic incidents, philosophical musings, reminiscences and anecdotes, all recorded in Sterne's delightful, meandering style.

430261 160pp £3.50

BRAM STOKER

1847–1912

Dracula

Edited with an introduction by Maurice Hindle

The first, and most chilling, portrait of the unbridled lusts and desires of a vampire is still the ultimate terror myth.

433813 560pp £2.50

WILLIAM THACKERAY

1811–1863

The History of Henry Esmond

Edited by John Sutherland and Michael Greenfield with an introduction by John Sutherland

This blend of psychological drama, romance and history is set during the reign of Queen Anne and examines the conflicts between England's Tory-Catholic past and its Whiggish-Protestant future.

430490 544pp £5.99

The History of Pendennis

Edited by Donald Hawes with an introduction by J I M Stewart

This novel of a young man's passage from miserable schoolboy to striving journalist, from carefree Oxbridge to the high (and low) life of London, mirrors Thackeray's own life.

430768 816pp £6.99

The Newcomes

Edited with an introduction by David Pascoe

In this autobiographical novel, Thackeray depicts the 'respectable' social world of London in the 1820s and '30s, a milieu where material wealth determined acceptability, and alliances, including marriage, were pursued with the goal of enhancing a family's position.

43481X 880pp £7.99

Vanity Fair

Edited with an introduction by J I M Stewart

Becky Sharp, one of the most resourceful, engaging and amoral women in literature, is the heroine of this sparkling satirical panorama of British society during the Napoleonic Wars.

430350 816pp £2.99

THREE GOTHIC NOVELS

Edited by Peter Fairclough with an introduction by Mario Praz

Horace Walpole's *The Castle of Otranto*, published in 1765 is the prototype of all Gothic novels; William Beckford's *Vathek* combines Gothic romanticism with Oriental exoticism; and Mary Shelley's *Frankenstein* is a masterpiece of Gothic horror.

430369 512pp £6.99

ANTHONY TROLLOPE

1815–1882

AN AUTOBIOGRAPHY

Edited with an introduction by David Skilton

As he recounts his journey from an impoverished, unhappy childhood to the fame and prosperity he achieved as a writer, Trollope writes not of moments of great inspiration but of hours of toil and dogged dedication to the trade of writing.

434054 320pp £5.99

BARCHESTER TOWERS

Edited and introduction by Robin Gilmour with a preface by J K Galbraith

In this second novel of the Barsetshire Chronicles series, Trollope continues the story begun in *The Warden* and explores the conflict between the High and Low Church during the mid-Victorian period.

432035 576pp £3.50

CAN YOU FORGIVE HER?

Edited with an introduction by Stephen Wall

The first of Trollope's Palliser novels is concerned with a spirited young woman in London who rejects her faultless fiancé to marry an aggressive opportunist, a decision Victorian society cannot accept.

430865 848pp £4.99

DR THORNE

Edited with an introduction by Ruth Rendell

One of Trollope's liveliest novels tells the story of Frank Greshman and Mary Thorne, who are intent on marriage despite Mary's ostensible poverty.

433260 592pp £3.99

THE DUKE'S CHILDREN

Edited with an introduction by Dinah Birch

The Duke's Children, the last of the six Palliser novels, brings to an end the story of Plantagenet Palliser, Trollope's favourite character among his fictional creations. Written when the author was sixty-one, the novel clearly embodies Trollope's reflections on his own life and family, the emerging independence of women, and the changes in British society and politics.

433449 560pp £3.99

THE EUSTACE DIAMONDS

Edited by Stephen Gill and John Sutherland

Trollope examines the many guises of 'truth' in this taut novel about Lizzie Eustace, a brave, beautiful and unscrupulous young woman.

430415 784pp £4.99

FRAMLEY PARSONAGE

Edited with an introduction by David Skilton and Peter Miles

In the fourth novel of the Barsetshire Chronicles series, a young Victorian clergyman's social ambitions lead him to the brink of ruin.

432132 576pp £3.50

He Knew He Was Right

Edited with an introduction by
Frank Kermode

Written at the time of heated controversy about women's emancipation, *He Knew He Was Right* examines the conflict between male fantasies of total possession and a married woman's right to a measure of independence.

433910 864pp £4.99

The Last Chronicle of Barset

Edited by Peter Fairclough with an introduction by Laurence Lerner

In the last of the Barsetshire novels, Trollope draws a moving portrait of a curate who, falsely accused of theft, suffers bitter humiliation.

430245 880pp £4.99

Phineas Finn

Edited with an introduction by
John Sutherland

The second of Trollope's *Palliser* novels tells of the career of a hot-blooded middle-class politician whose sexual energies bring him much success with women.

430857 752pp £4.50

The Prime Minister

Edited with an introduction by David Skilton

In this penultimate book in the *Palliser* series, Trollope chronicles Plantagenet Palliser's ascent to the highest office in the land and explores how the realities of political life challenge his scrupulously moral hero.

43349X 736pp £4.99

Rachel Ray

Edited with an introduction by
John Sutherland

Trollope's belief that reading novels was the ideal way for women to 'learn what was expected from them, and what they are to expect when lovers come' informs this charming depiction of the romance between Rachel Ray, an innocent young woman in a small, idyllic town, and Luke Rowan, a brash young man from London. The book captures in engaging detail the fluctuating moods of first love and also the reactions of those on the sidelines.

434100 368pp £5.99

The Small House at Allington

Edited with an introduction by
Julian Thompson

This story of Lily Dale and her love for the ambitious, self-seeking, faithless Crosbie offers a vivid portrayal of the social and political changes occurring in the mid-nineteenth century.

433252 752pp £3.99

The Warden

Edited with an introduction by
Robin Gilmour

The first book in the Barsetshire Chronicles tells the story of an elderly clergyman who resigns his church sinecure when it becomes the centre of public controversy.

432140 240pp £2.50

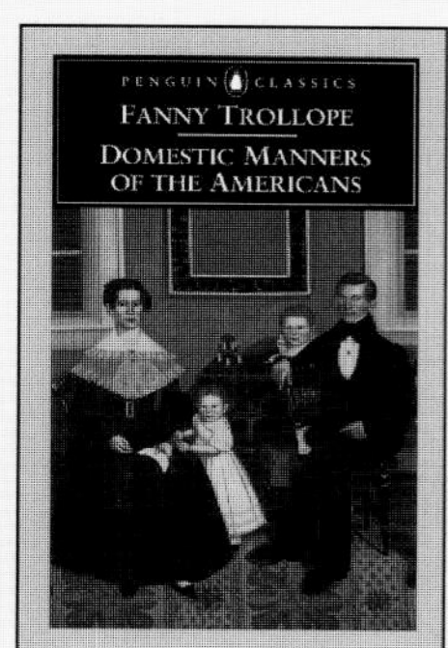

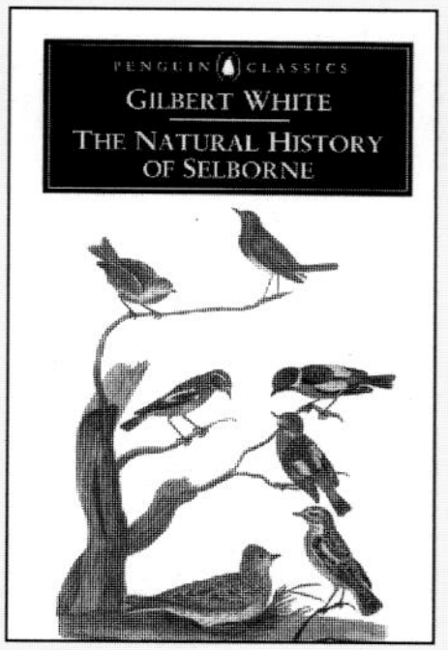

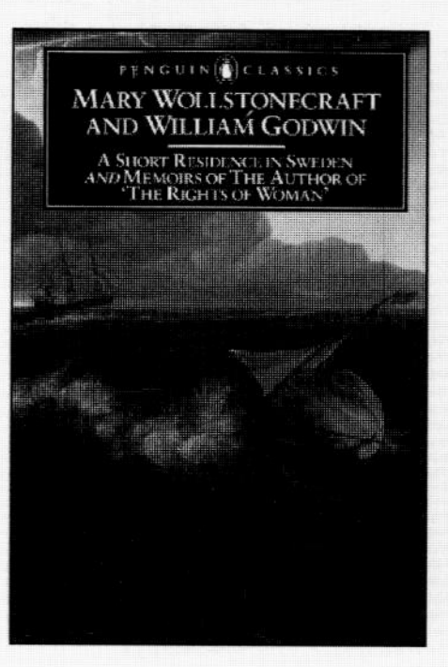

THE WAY WE LIVE NOW

Edited with an introduction by
Frank Kermode

First published in 1874 and widely regarded as the finest of all Trollope's novels, *The Way We Live Now* satirises to devastating effect the grip of the monetary ethic on politics, the aristocracy, the literary world, the London scene and the marriage market.

433929 816pp £3.99

FANNY TROLLOPE

1780–1863

DOMESTIC MANNERS OF THE AMERICANS

Edited with an introduction by
Pamela Neville-Singleton

Part satire, part masterpiece of nineteenth-century travel writing, this perceptive and humorous book grew from Fanny Trollope's ill-fated attempt to escape growing debts and the oppressively black moods of her husband by fleeing to the United States. After two miserable years she retreated to England, where she launched her remarkably successful literary career with this timeless and biting commentary on a society torn between high ideals and human frailities.

435611 416pp £8.99

GILBERT WHITE

1720–1793

THE NATURAL HISTORY OF SELBORNE

Edited with an introduction by
Richard Mabey

Gilbert White's beautifully written evocation of the natural world of Selborne has shaped our everyday view of the relations between human beings and nature, and remained enduringly popular since its first publication in 1788–9.

431128 320pp £2.99

MARY WOLLSTONECRAFT

1759–1797

VINDICATION OF THE RIGHTS OF WOMAN

Edited with an introduction by Miriam Brody

Published in 1792, this classic treatise applied the egalitarian principles of the French and American revolutions to the social, political and economic conditions of women.

433821 352pp £5.99

MARY WOLLSTONECRAFT AND WILLIAM GODWIN

A SHORT RESIDENCE IN SWEDEN, NORWAY AND DENMARK *AND* MEMOIRS OF THE AUTHOR OF A VINDICATION OF THE RIGHTS OF WOMAN

Edited with an introduction by
Richard Holmes

Feminist writer Wollstonecraft's record of her Scandinavian journey and her philosopher-husband's memoirs (written after her death) offer insight into the minds of two major figures in the transition from reason to romanticism in Europe.

432698 320pp £7.99

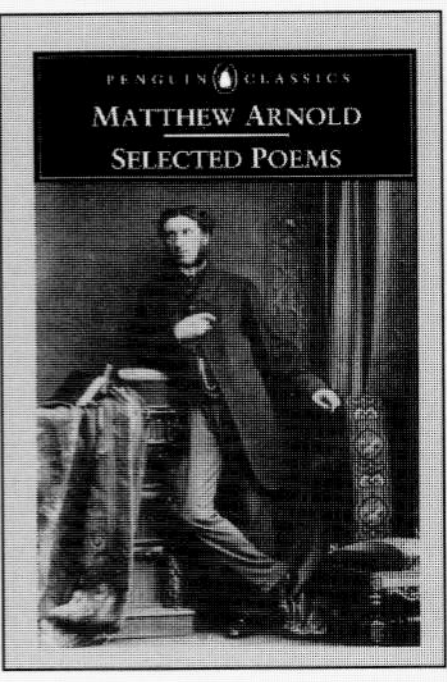

MARY WOLLSTONECRAFT AND MARY SHELLEY

Mary/Maria/Matilda

Edited with an introduction by Janet Todd

Three short novels written by mother and daughter offer insight into the personal lives of both authors as they illuminate struggles for identity within the early feminist movement.

433716 256pp £6.99

DOROTHY AND WILLIAM WORDSWORTH

Home at Grasmere

Edited by Colette Clark

This perceptive arrangement of Dorothy's journal entries alongside William's poems sheds light on the poet's creative process.

431365 304pp £6.99

PENGUIN ENGLISH POETS

GENERAL EDITOR CHRISTOPHER RICKS

'The virtue of the series is that it is the most comprehensive and most scholarly, simply the best range of editions of English poets now in existence – no other venture compares with it' Paul Keegan, Penguin Classics consultant editor

MATTHEW ARNOLD

1822–1888

Selected Poems

Edited with an introduction by Timothy Peltason

A selection of Arnold's best and most memorable poems, this collection includes such major works as 'Dover Beach' and 'Thyrsis' and the full texts of the long poems 'Empedocles on Etna', 'Sohrab and Rustum' and 'Tristram and Iseult'.

423761 256pp £6.99

WILLIAM BARNES

1801–1886

Selected Poems

Edited with notes by Andrew Motion

Elegiac and celebratory, the poems create incomparably vivid images of the nineteenth-century lives and landscapes of Barnes's native Dorset.

423796 192pp £6.99

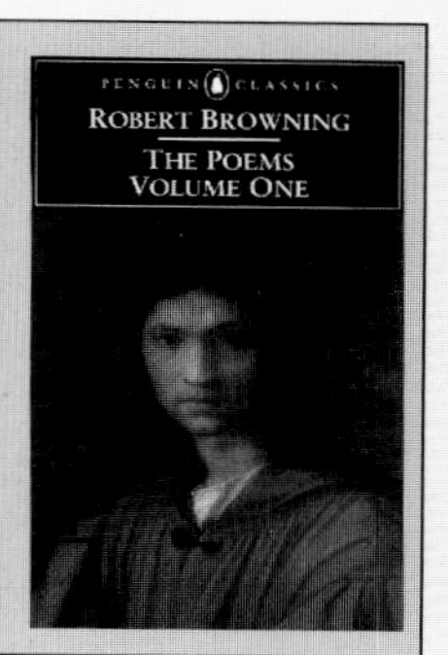

WILLIAM BLAKE

1757–1827

The Complete Poems

Edited by Alicia Ostriker

This edition contains all of Blake's poetry, with more than 150 pages of explanatory notes, including plot outlines of the more difficult poems, a chronology of Blake's life, a supplementary reading list, and a dictionary of proper names.

422153 1072pp £14.00

EMILY BRONTË

1818–1848

The Complete Poems

Edited with an introduction by
Janet Gezari

The first new edition of Brontë's poetry in half a century, here is a collection of twenty-one passionate poems, first published under a pseudonym in 1846.

423524 336pp £7.99

ELIZABETH BARRETT BROWNING

1806–1861

Aurora Leigh and Other Poems

Edited by John Robert Glorney Bolton
and Julia Bolton Holloway

'Her ardour and abundance, her brilliant descriptive powers, her shrewd and caustic humour infect us with her own enthusiasm.' *Aurora Leigh*, an epic story in blank verse, tells the story of the making of a woman poet, exploring the 'woman question', art and its relation to politics and social oppression.

434127 544pp £6.99

ROBERT BROWNING

1812–1889

The Poems

Edited by John Pettigrew, supplemented and completed by Thomas J Collins

This volume includes poems published posthumously, those previously unpublished and poems from the collection *Dramatic Romances and Lyrics*, *Men and Women*, and *Dramatis Personae*, all of which count as the masterpieces of a poet Henry James called a 'tremendous and incomparable modern'.

422595 1232pp £18.00

The Ring and the Book

Edited with an introduction by Richard Altick

This fully annotated version of Browning's *tour-de-force* of dramatic verse documents the 1698 trial of Count Guido Franceschini for the murder of his wife, who he accused of committing adultery with a young priest.

422943 712pp £14.99

ROBERT BURNS

1759–1796

Selected Poems

Edited by Carol McGuirk

Arranged in probable order of composition, and featuring both lyrics and tunes, this collection of poems and songs written by Burns late in his career reveals his emotional range for modern readers.

423826 368pp £6.99

LORD BYRON

1723–1786

Don Juan

Edited by T G Steffan, E Steffan and W W Pratt with an introduction by T G Steffan

In this rambling, exuberant, conversational poem, the travels of Don Juan are used as a vehicle for some of the most lively and acute commentaries on human societies and behaviour in the language. This edition is heavily annotated.

422161 768pp £15.00

Selected Poems

Edited with a preface by Susan J Wolfson and Peter J Manning

Flamboyant, brilliant and daring, relishing humour and irony, Byron's poetry reflects European Romanticism in an age of revolutions. Among the poems included are 'Childe Harold's Pilgrimage' and 'Sardanapalus'.

423818 864pp £7.99

LEWIS CARROLL

1832–1898

The Hunting of the Snark

Edited with an introduction by Martin Gardner

Inspired by the serendipitous line 'For the Snark was a Boojum, you see,' which occurred to him during a stroll, Lewis Carroll crafted a classic work of nonsense poetry that has intrigued readers for more than a century.

434917 128pp £5.99

JOHN CLARE

1793–1864

The Parish

Edited by Eric Robinson with notes by David Powell

John Clare was not only one of the finest English nature-poets but also a visionary and, in *The Parish*, a biting satirist and acid social observer. Clare's pictures of parish overseers, ranting preachers and windbag farmers are sharp and finely etched, created by a man who felt the full weight of their miserable tyranny.

432426 96pp £5.99

SAMUEL TAYLOR COLERIDGE

1772–1834

The Complete Poems

Edited by William Keach

This Penguin English Poets edition of the poetry of Coleridge contains the final texts of all the poems published in the poet's lifetime, together with a substantial selection from the verse still in manuscript on his death. William Keach's notes draw attention to significant variants, and important earlier versions of 'A Monody on the Death of Chatterton', 'The Eolian Harp', 'The Rime of the Ancient Mariner' and 'Dejection: An Ode' are included in full.

423532 656pp £11.00

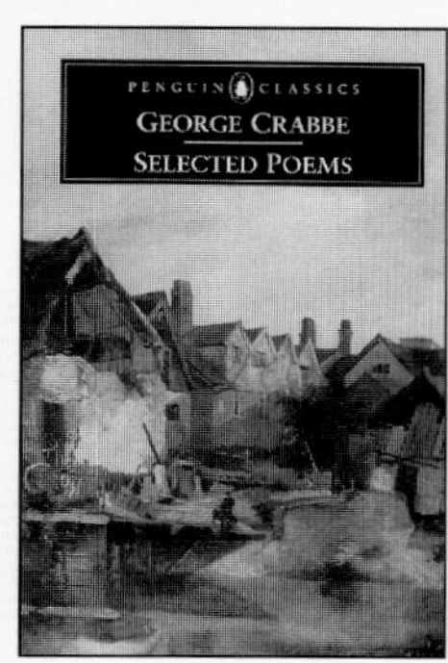

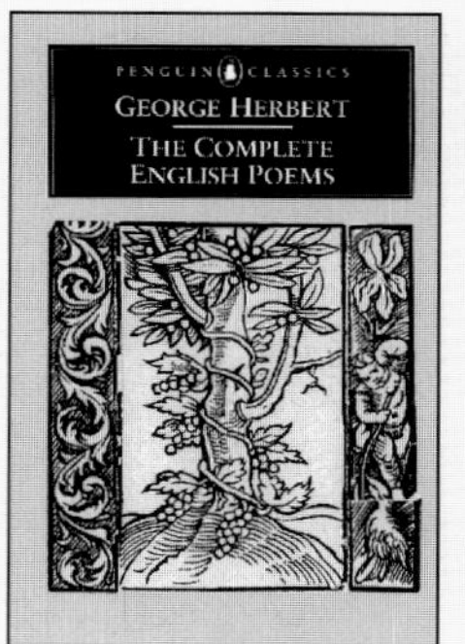

GEORGE CRABBE

1754–1832

SELECTED POEMS

Edited by Gavin Edwards

With his distinctive and original voice, Crabbe dramatizes human motive in the subtlest of language. This selection includes 'The Village', selections from 'The Borough' (including 'Peter Grimes'), the complete 'Tales of 1812', 'Delay Has Danger' from 'Tales of the Hall' and the remarkable late work 'The Family of Love'.

423656 528pp £8.99

JOHN DONNE

1572–1631

THE COMPLETE ENGLISH POEMS

Edited by A J Smith

'The first poet in the world in some things', is how John Donne was described by his contemporary Ben Jonson. Yet it is only in this century that he has been indisputably established as a great poet - and even, many feel, the greatest love poet of them all.

422099 688pp £9.99

JOHN DRYDEN

1631–1700

VIRGIL'S AENEID

Edited by Frederick M Keener

Dryden's *Æneis* (1697), writes Frederick Keener, is not merely a superb translation but 'an important, magisterial and moving English poem' in its own right, as well as a major influence on Pope and the main eighteenth-century tradition. This Penguin English Poets edition includes maps, a substantial glossary and enough background to help readers overcome any unfamiliarity with style or substance, thus making freshly accessible a work of enduring worth.

446273 480pp £9.99

THOMAS HARDY

1840–1928

SELECTED POEMS

Edited with a preface by Harry Thomas

Hardy abandoned the novel at the turn of the century, probably after public reaction to *Jude the Obscure*, but continued to write verse displaying a wide variety of metrical styles and stanza forms and a broad scope of tone and attitude. This definitive volume contains selections from his numerous collections published between 1898 and 1928.

433414 272pp £5.99

GEORGE HERBERT

1593–1633

THE COMPLETE ENGLISH POEMS

Edited with an introduction by John Tobin

The Temple, Herbert's masterpiece of worldly anguish and divine transcendence; his uncollected English verse; *A Priest to the Temple* (prose); and selections from Herbert's Latin poetry with translations form the basis of this volume.

423486 496pp £8.99

GERARD MANLEY HOPKINS

1844–1889

POEMS AND PROSE

Edited by W H Gardner

This edition contains verse wrought from the creative tensions and paradoxes of a poet-priest who strove to evoke the spiritual essence of nature sensuously. Besides such poems as 'The Wreck of the Deutschland', 'The Wind-hover' and 'God's Grandeur', this collection includes the 'terrible sonnets', numerous journal entries and Hopkins's letters to Robert Bridges.

420150 304pp £3.99

BEN JONSON

1572–1637

THE COMPLETE POEMS

Edited with a preface by George Parfitt

Nearly 400 works display the characteristic blend of classical and contemporary ideals that imbues Jonson's work, including 'Epigrams', 'The Forest', 'Underwoods: Miscellaneous Poems', 'Horace', 'The Art of Poetry' and 'Timber: Or Discoveries'.

422773 640pp £13.00

JOHN KEATS

1795–1821

THE COMPLETE POEMS

Edited by John Barnard

In addition to all the poems and plays known to be written by the archetypal romantic poet, this edition includes long extracts from Keats's letters, his annotations to *Paradise Lost*, and two poems and a play fragment that have been attributed to him.

422102 752pp £9.99

CHRISTOPHER MARLOWE

1564–1593

THE COMPLETE POEMS AND TRANSLATIONS

Edited by Stephen Orgel

All Marlowe's poems and translations are presented in a conservatively modernized text along with two contemporary continuations of 'Hero and Leander' and several replies to 'The Passionate Shepherd'.

422676 288pp £8.99

ANDREW MARVELL

1621–1678

THE COMPLETE POEMS

Edited by Elizabeth Story Donno

Based on recent studies of existing manuscripts, this collection of works by the seventeenth-century poet much admired by T S Eliot includes modern translations of Marvell's Greek and Latin poems, as well as his works in English.

422137 320pp £8.99

JOHN MILTON

1608–1674

THE COMPLETE POEMS

Edited with a preface and notes by John Leonard

John Milton was a master of almost every style of verse, from pastoral, devotional and

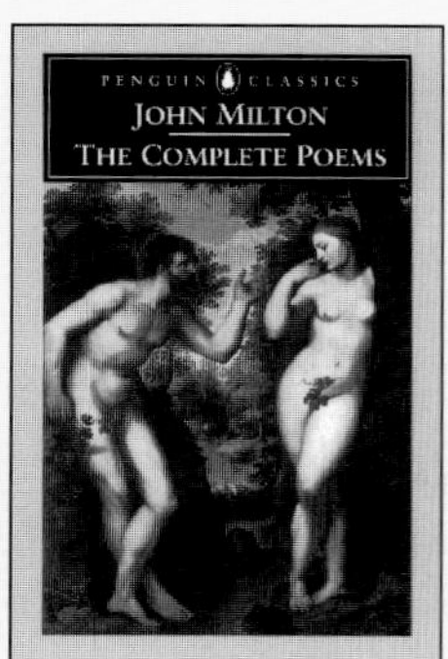

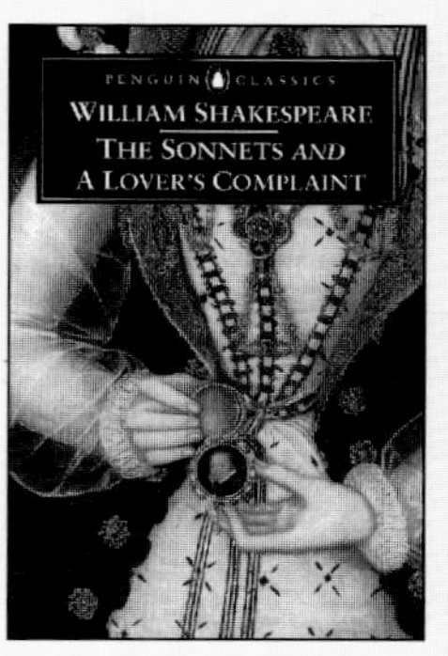

tenderly lyrical to the supreme grandeur of his great epic *Paradise Lost* and his biblical 'Greek tragedy' *Samson Agonistes*.

In this Penguin English Poets edition, John Leonard has modernized spelling, capitalization and any punctuation likely to cause confusion. For all readers seriously wanting to get to grips with one of the giants of English literature, there could be no better place to start.

433635 1024pp £11.99

NEW JULY 98

Paradise Lost

Edited with an introduction by
Christopher Ricks

Milton's fiery genius in pursuit of his great theme, to 'justify the ways of God to men', made *Paradise Lost* a masterpiece and one of the most controversial and enthralling poems ever written.

42363X 336pp £4.99

ALEXANDER POPE

1688–1744

The Iliad

Translated by Alexander Pope
Edited by Steven Shankman

Pope spent his formative years as a poet translating Homer, beginning with the *Iliad*, and in his translation he successfully found a style that answers the sublimity and grace of Homer.

445048 1248pp £15.99

WILLIAM SHAKESPEARE

1564–1616

The Narrative Poems

Venus and Adonis

The Rape of Lucrece

The Phoenix and the Turtle

The Passionate Pilgrim

Edited with an introduction and notes by
Maurice Evan

This fully annotated collection reveals a poet perhaps unrivalled in his ability to bring powerful expression to the most varied themes and sentiments.

436839 272pp £6.99

NEW AUGUST 98

The Sonnets *and* A Lover's Complaint

Edited by John Kerrigan

Shakespeare's masterpieces of wit and elaborate erotic word-play touch on such enduring themes as sexual desire, the pangs and torments of love, the aspirations of art, and the depredations of Time. They cannot fail to engage the imaginations of every reader who encounters them today.

436847 464pp £6.99

NEW APRIL 99

COMPLETE NEW PENGUIN SHAKESPEARE LISTING FEATURED ON PAGE 177

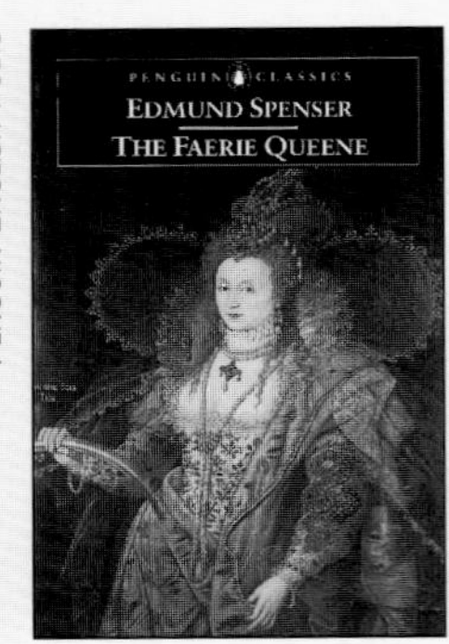

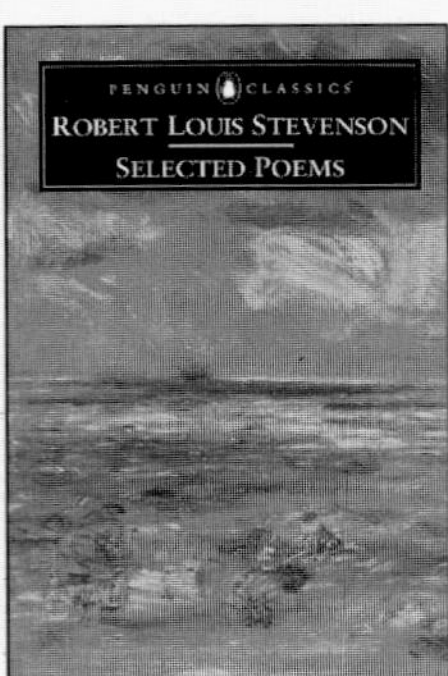

CHRISTOPHER SMART

1722–1771

SELECTED POEMS

Edited by Karina Williamson and Marcus Walsh

One of the most startlingly original poets of the eighteenth century, Smart produced some of his finest hymns, psalms and religious poems (including 'A Song to David') while confined to asylums or debtors' prison.

423672 416pp £8.99

EDMUND SPENSER

1522–1599

THE FAERIE QUEENE

Edited by Thomas P Roche Jr with C Patrick O'Donnell Jr

The first English-language epic, Spenser's masterful extended allegory of knightly virtue and supreme grace brilliantly unites medieval romance to Renaissance epic.

422072 1248pp £16.00

ROBERT LOUIS STEVENSON

1850–1894

SELECTED POEMS

Edited by Angus Calder

Fascinated by a wide variety of verse techniques, Robert Louis Stevenson produced superb work in styles ranging from folk ballads to witty conversational offerings for his friends. This definitive anthology captures a compelling and utterly individual voice.

435484 320pp £7.99

NEW JULY 98

ALFRED LORD TENNYSON

1809–1892

IDYLLS OF THE KING

Edited by J M Gray

For Tennyson, the *Idylls* embodied the universal and unending war between sense and soul, and *Arthur* the highest ideals of manhood and kingship, an attitude in keeping with the moral outlook of his day.

422536 384pp £9.99

SELECTED POEMS

Edited by Aidan Day

From a genius at painting human emotions in rich and sensuous imagery, this volume focuses on *In Memoriam* (1850), a record of spiritual conflict considered to be Tennyson's greatest work.

445455 400pp £6.99

THOMAS TRAHERNE

1637–1674

SELECTED POEMS AND PROSE

Edited with a preface by Alan Bradford

In poems from the Dobell folio and selections from his prose masterpiece, *Centuries of Meditations*, Traherne explores the boundless potential of the human mind and spirit as he celebrates the wonder and simplicity of the child.

445439 416pp £9.99

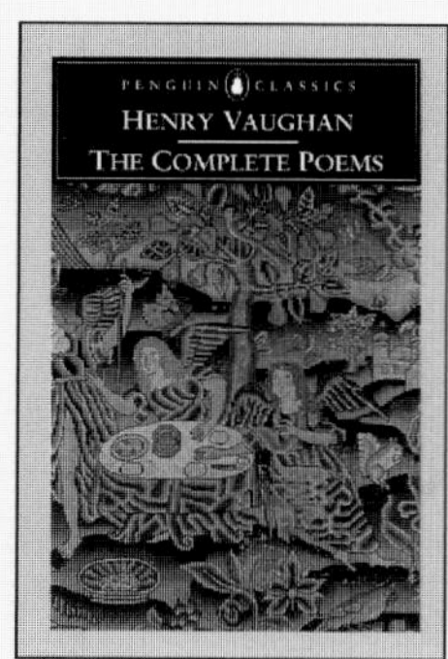

HENRY VAUGHAN

1621–1695

The Complete Poems

Edited by Alan Rudrum

Less worldly than Donne or Herbert, to whom he is indebted, Vaughan wrote poetry that is both mysterious and richly suggestive. His approach to Christianity, however, cannot be given precise and indisputable definition, as he was strongly influenced by hermeticism and other prevailing philosophies. In addition, his response to nature prefigures nineteenth-century romanticism.

422080 720pp £9.99

JOHN WILMOT, EARL OF ROCHESTER

1647–1680

The Complete Works

Edited with an introduction by Frank H Ellis

This volume encompasses the works of the Earl of Rochester – the Restoration's infamous literary rake, hedonist and master of satire – and includes tragic verse, prose comedy, boisterous songs, rich rhymes and language, and frank explorations of sexual matters.

423621 488pp £9.99

WILLIAM WORDSWORTH

1770–1850

The Poems Volume 1

Edited with an introduction by John O Hayden

The poems, arranged in chronological order, show the coherent whole of Wordsworth's lifework, the parts of which are a single and organic opus of autobiographical confession depicting the growth of a poet's sensibility.

422110 1072pp £16.00

The Poems Volume 2

Edited with an introduction by John O Hayden

422129 1104pp £16.00

The Prelude: The Four Texts

1798, 1799, 1805, 1850

Edited by Jonathan Wordsworth

Containing the two-book *Prelude* of 1799 as well as the complete 1805 and 1850 versions, this is a comprehensive new volume edited by Jonathan Wordsworth.

433694 736pp £9.99

Selected Poems

Edited by John O Hayden

This new, generous selection of Wordsworth's best poems, freshly edited and chronologically arranged, concentrates on his greater short works.

423753 624pp £7.99

SIR THOMAS WYATT

1503–1542

The Complete Poems

Edited with a preface by R A Rebholz

The rondeaux, sonnets, epigrams, canzoni, ballades, songs, epistolary satires, psalms and poems of Renaissance diplomat and Tudor courtier Sir Thomas Wyatt express a high degree of intelligence and culture as surely as did his diplomatic work.

422277 560pp £12.50

POETRY ANTHOLOGIES

THE EARLIEST ENGLISH POEMS

Translated with an introduction by
Michael Alexander

This select volume includes translations of heroic poems (including the oldest poem in the English language), a passage from *Beowulf*, 'riddles' from *The Exeter Book*, and elegies in Anglo-Saxon metre and alliteration.

445943 192pp £7.99

ENGLISH ROMANTIC VERSE

Edited with an introduction by
David Wright

Nearly all the famous and beloved master-works can be found here – 'Intimations of Immortality', 'Rime of The Ancient Mariner' and 'The Tyger' – as well as some less familiar poems from such writers as Christopher Smart, Walter Savage Landor, John Clare and Thomas Lovell Beddoes.

421025 384pp £7.99

THE GOLDEN TREASURY

Edited with an introduction by Christopher Ricks and selected with notes by Francis Turner Palgrave

Unrivalled as the paradigm of Victorian poetry anthologies, the *Treasury* includes some of the finest English lyric verse from the Elizabethan era to the mid-nineteenth century.

423648 544pp £7.99

THE METAPHYSICAL POETS

Edited with an introduction by
Helen Gardner

This selection features thirty-eight poets, among them Carew, Crashaw, Donne, Herbert, Jonson, Lovelace, Marvell, Suckling and Vaughan.

42038X 336pp £6.99

THE PENGUIN BOOK OF RENAISSANCE VERSE

1509–1659

Selected with an introduction by
David Norbrook
Edited by H R Woudhuysen

Organized thematically, this superbly edited anthology offers a new view of one of the most fertile periods in the history of English literature. Generous space is devoted to writings of women, works of popular culture and regional non courtly poetry.

42346X 976pp £11.99

THE PENGUIN BOOK OF RESTORATION VERSE

Edited with an introduction by Harold Love

This volume is arranged by theme and selects from the best poetry written between 1660–1700, decades of momentous political experiment in England. Less inhibited than the Jacobeans, more vigorous than the Augustans, the Restoration poets comment exhilaratingly on a society as pragmatic and questioning as our own.

424075 384pp £9.99

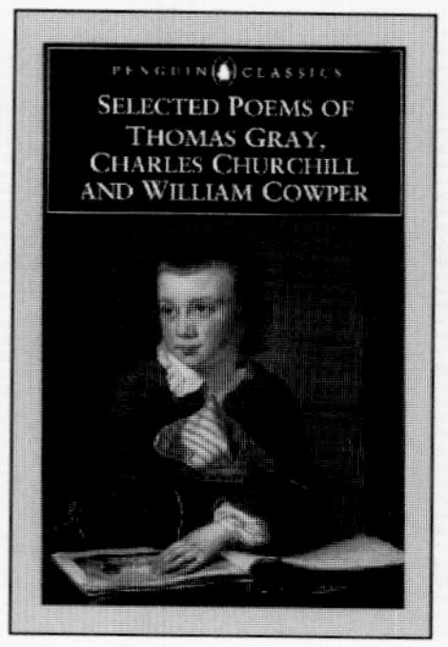

THE PENGUIN BOOK OF VICTORIAN VERSE

Selected and edited by Daniel Karlin

Daniel Karlin has selected poetry written and published during the reign of Queen Victoria, 1837–1901. Giving pride of place to Tennyson, Robert Browning and Christina Rossetti, the volume offers generous selections from other major poets such as Arnold, Emily Brontë, Hardy and Hopkins. It is notable, too, for its discovery and inclusion of eccentric, dissenting, un-Victorian voices, poets who squarely refuse to 'represent' their period.

445781 928pp £10.99

NEW OCTOBER 98

POETRY OF THE 1890s

Edited with an introduction by
R K R Thornton and Marion Thain

This new edition of the acclaimed *Poetry of the 1890s* clarifies the myths of the 'naughty nineties', the sensational Decadent and the muscular Counter-Decadent by setting them within the astonishing variety and range of the poetry of the period. This volume also includes two new sections on women poets.

436391 368pp £8.99

SELECTED POEMS OF ABRAHAM COWLEY, EDMUND WALLER AND JOHN OLDHAM

Edited with an introduction by Julia Griffin

The combined lives of the three poets in this volume span most of the seventeenth century, a period of violent political and social change.

424040 224pp £8.99

NEW AUGUST 98

SELECTED POEMS OF THOMAS GRAY, CHARLES CHURCHILL AND WILLIAM COWPER

Edited with an introduction by
Katherine Turner

The major 'Pre-Romantic' poets form a vital link between the age of Pope, who died in 1744, and the very different era which opened with the publication of Wordsworth's and Coleridge's *Lyrical Ballads* (1798). Together, they represent the voice of the 'Age of Sensibility', which deeply influenced the writers of the Romantic generation even as they reacted against them. This new English Poets edition makes freshly available a superb selection of their work.

424016 240pp £8.99

SELECTED POEMS OF ROBERT HENRYSON AND WILLIAM DUNBAR

Edited with an introduction by Douglas Gray

Robert Henryson and William Dunbar are the most powerful and individual voices in the Scottish poetry of the Middle Ages.

42248X 432pp £8.99

NEW OCTOBER 98

POETS IN TRANSLATION

This successful Penguin series offers the best translations in English, through the centuries, of the major Classical and European poets. With full introductions and notes, and with a wide range of work amply represented, these coherent anthologies are tributes that continue to live.

BAUDELAIRE IN ENGLISH

Edited by Carol Clark and Robert Sykes

In his psychological and sexual complexity, images of alienation and fascination with the outcasts of urban life, Charles Baudelaire (1821–67) was a pioneering modern spirit who has proved profoundly influential well beyond the borders of France.

This superb anthology brings together the translations of his poetry and 'prose poems' which best reveal the different facets of Baudelaire's personality.

446443 336pp £9.99

HOMER IN ENGLISH

Edited by George Steiner

From Chaucer's *Troilus and Criseyde* and Pound's *Cantos* to Joyce's *Ulysses* and Walcott's *Omeros*, Homer has been the most translated author in Western literature. This superb selection assembles the best translations from six and a half centuries.

446214 400pp £9.99

HORACE IN ENGLISH

Edited by Donald Carne-Ross

This anthology brings together a diverse group of Latin-to-English translations of Horace's *Odes*, *Epodes*, *Satires* and *Epistles*. It contains well-known translations, as well as ones that reflect the conventions and poetic style of the translator's own time or that offer fresh readings of Horace's centuries-old masterpieces.

423877 576pp £9.99

MARTIAL IN ENGLISH

Edited by John Sullivan and Anthony Boyle

Bringing together translations or adaptations of Martial's epigrams from the sixteenth to the twentieth centuries, *Martial in English* will amuse, enlighten and shock contemporary readers.

423893 480pp £9.99

OVID IN ENGLISH

Edited by Christopher Martin

Witty, erotic, sceptical and subversive, Ovid has been a seminal presence in English literature from the time of Chaucer and Caxton to Ted Hughes and Seamus Heaney. This superb collection brings together complete elegies from the *Amores*, *Heroides* and *Poems of Exile*, as well as many self-contained episodes from longer works, revealing both the sheer variety of Ovid's genius and the range of his impact on the British imagination.

446699 464pp £9.99

NEW JUNE 98

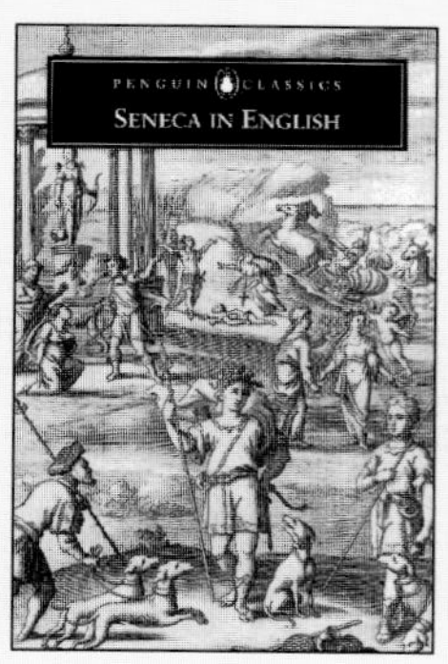

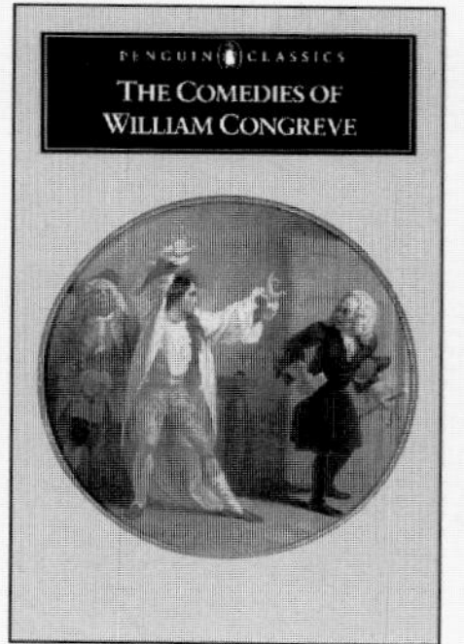

THE PSALMS IN ENGLISH

Edited by Donald Davie

This collection brings together British versions of the *Psalms* from the sixteenth century to contemporary times and includes contributions from Wyatt, Shakespeare, Donne, Hardy, Kipling, Longfellow, and Pound, among many others.

446184 448pp £9.99

SENECA IN ENGLISH

Edited by Don Share

Playwright and philosopher Seneca the Younger wrote in a violent, epigrammatic and extreme style. His works were imitated by writers ranging from Jonson to Johnson, from Milton to Marvel, and, in our own turbulent century, they have also inspired T S Eliot, Robert Lowell and Ted Hughes. This superb selection of translations, adaptations and variations vividly demonstrates Seneca's powerful continuing presence in English poetry.

446672 288pp £9.99

VIRGIL IN ENGLISH

Edited by K W Gransden

For T S Eliot, Virgil was not merely one of the great masters but 'our classic, the classic of all Europe'. Perhaps no other writer has generated a longer and larger tradition of commentary, translation and imitation. This selection consists largely of straight translations, along with a number of pieces illustrating Virgil's influence; celebrated episodes like the death of Dido, and Aeneas's descent into the underworld, appear in several different versions.

423869 384pp £9.99

PLAYS

WILLIAM CONGREVE

1670–1729

THE COMEDIES

The Old Bachelor

The Double Dealer

Love for Love

The Way of the World

Edited with an introduction by Eric S Rump

These Restoration comedies of manners depict the shallow world of 'society' where the right artifice in manners, fashion and money create success.

432310 416pp £7.99

JOHN GAY

1685–1732

THE BEGGAR'S OPERA

Edited with an introduction by
Bryan Loughrey and T O Treadwell

This witty parody of Italian opera, featuring the denizens of the British underworld, was performed more than any other play during the eighteenth century.

432205 128pp £5.99

BEN JONSON

1572–1637

Three Comedies

Volpone/The Alchemist/Bartholomew Fair

Edited by Michael Jamieson

Shakespeare's nearest rival created in *Volpone* and *The Alchemist* hilarious portraits of cupidity and chicanery, while in *Bartholomew Fair* he portrays his fellow Londoners at their most festive – and most bawdy.

43013X 496pp £5.99

CHRISTOPHER MARLOWE

1564–1593

The Complete Plays

Dido Queen of Carthage/Tamburlaine the Great/ Doctor Faustus/The Jew of Malta/Edward II/ The Massacre of Paris

Edited with an introduction by J B Steane

Marlowe has always attracted controversy. At one extreme he is considered an atheist rebel and at the other a Christian traditionalist, a divergence which is reflected in the extraordinary range of his plays.

430377 608pp £7.99

THOMAS MIDDLETON

1580–1627

Five Plays

A Trick to Catch the Old One/ The Revenger's Tragedy/ A Chaste Maid in Cheapside/Women Beware Women/The Changeling

Edited with an introduction by Bryan Loughrey and Neil Taylor

Ranging from ingenious comedy to powerful tragedy, these five plays portray the corruptive effects of politics and love in Elizabethan London.

432191 464pp £8.99

SHAKESPEARE

1564–1616

Four Comedies

The Taming of the Shrew/As You Like It/ Twelfth Night/A Midsummer Night's Dream

Edited with introductions and notes by G R Hibbard, Stanley Wells, H J Oliver and M M Mahood

This collection is engagingly introduced and skilfully annotated, and brings together four of Shakespeare's most spirited comedies.

434542 688pp £7.99

COMPLETE NEW PENGUIN SHAKESPEARE LISTING FEATURED ON PAGE 177

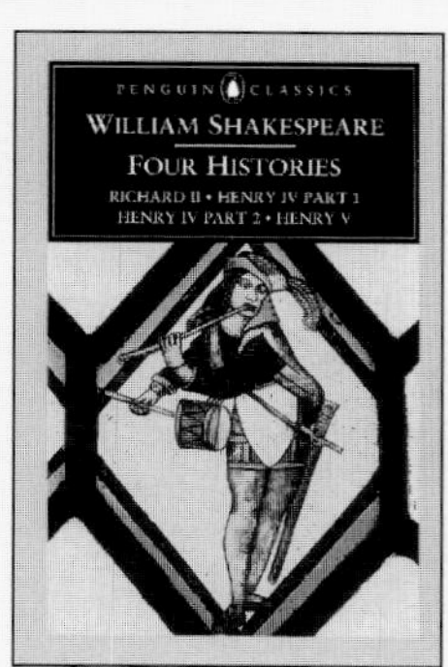

Four Histories

Richard II/Henry IV Part One/ Henry IV Part Two/Henry V

Edited with introductions and notes by Stanley Wells, P H Davison and A R Humphreys

Shakespeare explores matters of honour, history, tradition and change in this cycle of plays chronicling the turbulent transition of the British monarchy.

43450X 880pp £6.99

Four Tragedies

Hamlet/Othello/King Lear/Macbeth

Edited with introductions and notes by T J B Spencer, Anne Barton, Kenneth Muir and G K Hunter

These four tragedies contain some of Shakespeare's most celebrated protagonists and finest dramatic poetry.

434585 960pp £7.99

Three Roman Plays

Julius Caesar/Coriolanus/Anthony and Cleopatra

Edited with introductions and notes by Norman Sanders, Emrys Jones and G R Hibbard

Each of these plays, previously published separately in the New Penguin Shakespeare series, investigates political action and the relationship between the personal and the political.

434615 672pp £6.99

RICHARD BRINSLEY SHERIDAN

1751–1816

The School for Scandal and Other Plays

The Rivals/The Critic/School for Scandal

Edited with an introduction by Eric S Rump

Ingenious plots, agile and eloquent wit, and an unerring eye for the comic situation characterize Sheridan's drama. Never an insistent moralist, he delighted in deflating hypocrisy and in satirizing the manners of his age.

43240X 288pp £6.99

JOHN WEBSTER

c. 1580–1634

Three Plays

The White Devil/The Duchess of Malfi/ The Devil's Law-Case

Introduction and notes by David C Gunby

This sampling of plays shows Webster to be a superb playwright, able to exploit cruelty and horror to their full theatrical potential. Beneath the apparent anarchy of the plays, however, is a profoundly religious belief in the moral nature of the universe.

430814 464pp £7.99

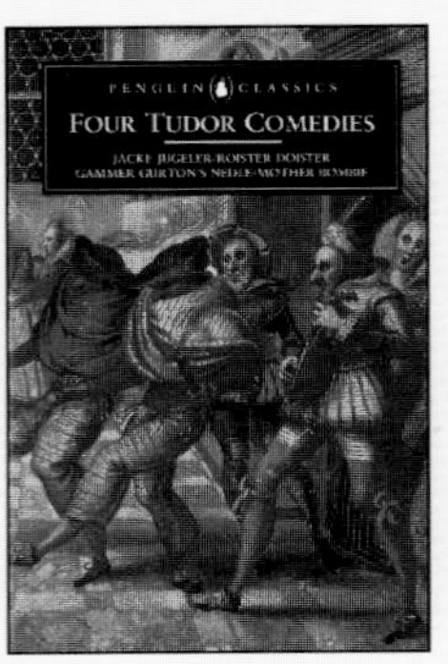

COLLECTIONS

ENGLISH MYSTERY PLAYS

A Selection

Edited with an introduction by Peter Happé

These thirty-seven mystery plays, written during the late medieval period to celebrate the Christian story from Creation to Doomsday – with two central peaks in the *Nativity* and the *Passion of Christ* – significantly influenced the work of later dramatists.

430938 720pp £8.99

FOUR ENGLISH COMEDIES

The Way of the World – Congreve

Volpone – Jonson

She Stoops to Conquer – Goldsmith

The School for Scandal – Sheridan

Edited by J M Morrell

Four classics of English comedy in the seventeenth and eighteenth centuries. Although very different, these plays are collected together in one volume by reason of their universality. They will delight audiences today as much as they did when first performed.

431586 416pp £6.99

FOUR TUDOR COMEDIES

Jacke Jugeler

Roister Doister

Gammer Gurton's Nedle

Mother Bombie

Edited with an introduction by
William Tydeman

These Tudor comedies are plays of wonderful art and exuberance and deserve rediscovery by present-day actors, audiences and readers.

436634 448pp £9.99

THREE JACOBEAN TRAGEDIES

The Changeling – Middleton & Rowley

The Revenger's Tragedy – Tourneur

The White Devil – Webster

Edited with an introduction by
Gamini Salgado

From the early seventeenth century, three of the finest examples of Jacobean revenge tragedy make up this collection.

430067 368pp £7.99

THREE RESTORATION COMEDIES

The Man of Mode – Etherege

The Country Wife – Wycherley

Love for Love – Congreve

Edited with an introduction by
Gamini Salgado

Artificial, irreverent and bawdy, the Restoration theatre came as a violent reaction to the strict ordinance of the Commonwealth.

43027X 368pp £6.99

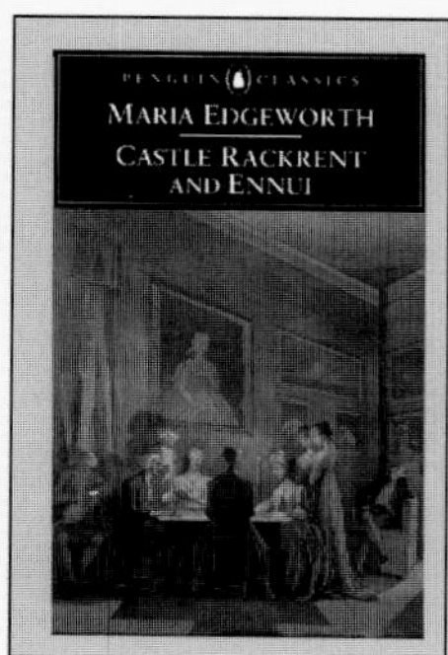

IRISH LITERATURE

MARIA EDGEWORTH

1768–1849

CASTLE RACKRENT *AND* ENNUI

Edited with an introduction by Marilyn Butler

Stylish and cosmopolitan, heir to Swift's fantasy and wit, Maria Edgeworth's fiction explores the relations of England and Ireland at a time of historical crisis. 'When *Castle Rackrent* and *Ennui* are paired, they read as perhaps the boldest, most innovative and most influential contribution to English language fiction by a woman writer before Charlotte Brontë and George Eliot' Marilyn Butler

433201 368pp £2.50

JONATHAN SWIFT

1667–1745

GULLIVER'S TRAVELS

Edited by Peter Dixon and John Chalker with an introduction by Michael Foot

Swift's satirical account of Gulliver's visits to Lilliput and Brobdingnag has amused and provoked readers since it was first published in 1726. A profound comment on the Age of Reason, it is perhaps the finest satire in the English language.

430229 368pp £2.50

OSCAR WILDE

1854–1900

THE COMPLETE SHORT FICTION

Edited with an introduction by Ian Small

This volume gathers the short masterpieces that brought Wilde his first fame as a writer of fiction and includes the complete texts of *The Happy Prince and Other Tales*, *A House of Pomegranates*, *Lord Arthur Savile's Crime and Other Stories*, 'Poems in Prose' and 'Portrait of Mr W H'.

434232 336pp £2.50

DE PROFUNDIS AND OTHER WRITINGS

Introduction by Hesketh Pearson

This collection contains many examples of Wilde's humorous and epigrammatic genius that captured the London theatre and, by suddenly casting light from an unexpected angle, widened the bounds of truth. Included are 'The Soul of Man Under Socialism', 'The Decay of Lying', and a selection of poems, including *The Ballad of Reading Gaol*, 'Sonnet to Liberty', 'Requiescat' and 'To My Wife'.

43089X 256pp £4.99

NOTHING ... EXCEPT MY GENIUS

Compiled by Alastair Rolfe

Introductory essay 'Playing Oscar' by Stephen Fry

This new selection is drawn from Wilde's stories, novels, plays, lectures, reviews and letters, and provides an invaluable introduction and reference to Wilde the artist and the man.

436936 112pp £2.99

THE PICTURE OF DORIAN GRAY

Edited with an introduction by Peter Ackroyd

First published to scandal and protest in 1891, this story of a flamboyant hedonist is a sterling example of Wilde's wit and aestheticism.

43187X 272pp £2.50

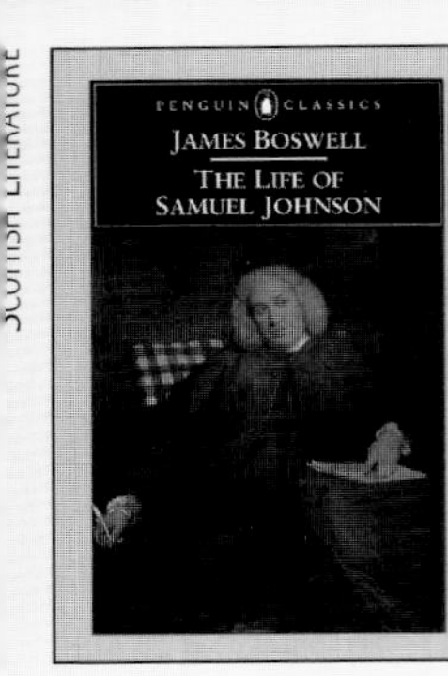

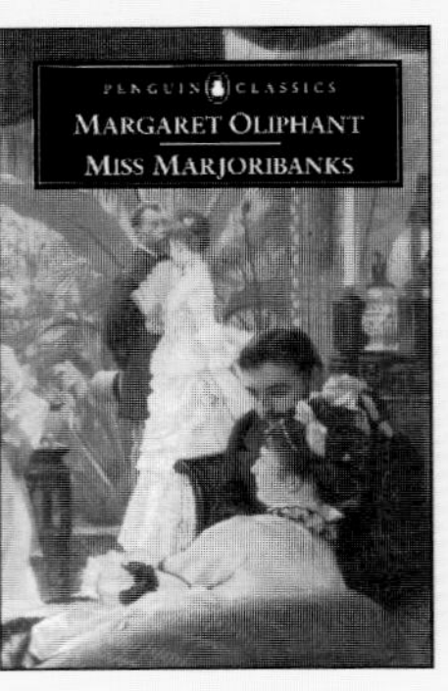

SCOTTISH LITERATURE

JAMES BOSWELL

1740–1795

The Life of Samuel Johnson

Edited and abridged with an introduction by Christopher Hibbert

This classic biography completed in 1791 is based on Boswell's conversations with Johnson, documents and letters and anecdotes from friends.

431160 384pp £7.99

SAMUEL JOHNSON AND JAMES BOSWELL

A Journey to the Western Isles of Scotland *and* The Journal of a Tour of the Hebrides

Edited with an introduction by Peter Levi

The remarkable friendship between Johnson and Boswell is celebrated in these complementary journals written during their tour of Scotland in 1773.

432213 432pp £6.99

JAMES HOGG

1770–1835

The Private Memoirs and Confessions of a Justified Sinner

Edited with an introduction by John Wain

Through a supernatural tale in which the Calvinist doctrine of predestination allows a devout young man to rationalize murder, James Hogg reflects the moral and religious tensions of early nineteenth-century British society.

431985 256pp £4.99

MARGARET OLIPHANT

1828–1897

Miss Marjoribanks

Edited with an introduction by Elisabeth Jay

'A tour de force ... full of wit, surprises and intrigue ... ' wrote Q. D. Leavis, who declared Margaret Oliphant's heroine Lucilla Marjoribanks to be the 'missing link' in Victorian literature between Jane Austen's Emma and George Eliot's Dorothea Brooke, and 'more entertaining, more impressive and more likeable than either'.

436308 352pp £6.99

NEW AUGUST 98

WALTER SCOTT

1771–1832

The Antiquary

Edited by David Hewitt, with an introduction by David Punter

With its vivid drama and exuberant pace, *The Antiquary* confirms Scott's reputation as the great storyteller of modern Europe.

436529 512pp £7.99

NEW JANUARY 99

The Heart of Mid-Lothian

Edited with an introduction by Anthony A H Inglis

The inventor and master of the historical novel tells the story of a determined heroine's dramatic confrontation with the justice system in a trial for infanticide, mixing historical fact with folklore from the uneasy, changing world of 1730s Scotland.

431292 864pp £3.99

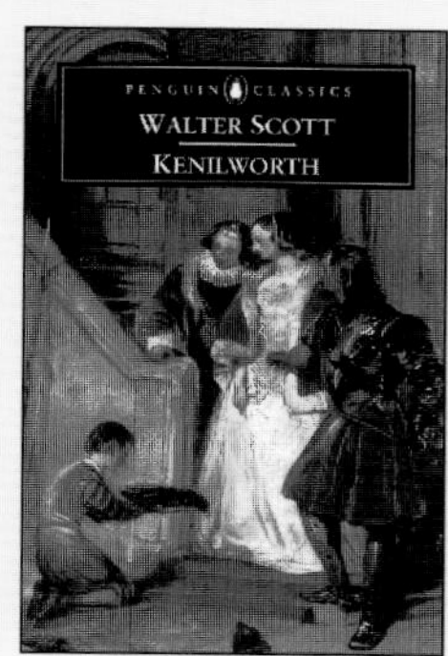

IVANHOE

Edited with an introduction
and notes by A N Wilson

A stirring and exciting re-creation of the age of chivalry, alive with such legends as Richard the Lion-Heart and Robin Hood, this is Scotland's most popular novel.

431438 624pp £3.99

KENILWORTH

Edited with an introduction by J H Alexander

Scott's magnificent novel recreates the drama, assurance and profound unease of the Age of Elizabeth through the story of Amy Robsart. Rich in character, melodrama and romance, *Kenilworth* is rivalled only by the great Elizabethan dramas.

436545 528pp £6.99
NEW JANUARY 99

THE TALE OF OLD MORTALITY

Edited with an introduction by
Douglas Mack

Scott's undisputed masterpiece distils the humour, grit and romance of the West of Scotland, past and present. 'I am complete master of the whole history of these strange times,' Scott declared in the course of writing *Old Mortality*, 'so I trust I have come decently off for as Falstaff very reasonably asks is not the *truth* the *truth*.'

436537 496pp £6.99
NEW JANUARY 99

ROB ROY

An adventure tale filled with brave deeds and cowardly conspiracies, noble heroes and despicable traitors, *Rob Roy* sweeps readers into the turmoil that erupted in England and Scotland after the death of Queen Anne. Based on the real-life Rob Roy MacGregor, it explores a common theme in Scott's work: the disappearance of the heroic values of chivalry as society became more ordered and prosperous.

435549 512pp £4.99

WAVERLEY

Edited with an introduction by Andrew Hook

This highly readable story of a young man involved in the Jacobite Rebellion of 1754 blends realism and romance in a classic example of Scott's 'invention' – the historical novel.

430717 608pp £4.99

ADAM SMITH

1723–1790

THE WEALTH OF NATIONS

Books I–III

Edited with an introduction by
Andrew Skinner

In this work, which laid the foundations of economic theory in general and of 'classical' economics in particular, Smith pinpointed the division of labour as a major explanation of economic growth.

432086 544pp £6.99

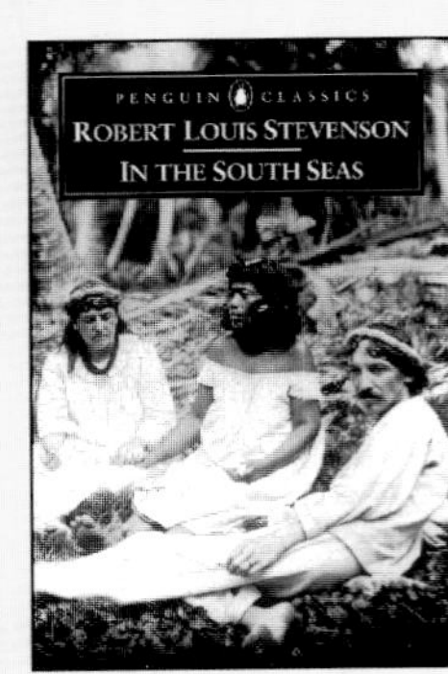

ROBERT LOUIS STEVENSON

1850–1894

In the South Seas

Edited with an introduction by Neil Rennie

In the South Seas records Stevenson's travels with his family in the Marquesas, the Paumotus and the Gilbert Islands during 1888–9. Its combination of personal anecdote and historical account, of autobiography and anthropology, of Stevenson and the South Sea islands, has a particular charm.

434364 336pp £6.99

NEW OCTOBER 98

Kidnapped

Edited with an introduction by Donald McFarlan

Set in the aftermath of the Jacobite Rebellion of 1745, *Kidnapped* is a swashbuckling adventure tale of family treachery, abduction and murder.

434011 272pp £2.99

The Master of Ballantrae

Edited with an introduction by Adrian Poole

In the ancestral home of the Duries, a family divided by the Jacobite risings of 1745, two brothers, James and Henry, carry out a fatal rivalry over a wealthy and beautiful kinswoman who loves one brother but marries the other.

434461 288pp £3.99

Selected Poems

Edited by Angus Calder

Fascinated by a wide variety of verse techniques, Robert Louis Stevenson produced superb work in styles ranging from folk ballads to witty conversational offerings for his friends. This definitive anthology captures a compelling and utterly individual voice.

435484 320pp £7.99

NEW JULY 98

The Strange Case of Dr Jekyll and Mr Hyde and Other Stories

Edited with an introduction by Jenni Calder

This volume also includes two later stories set in the South Seas, 'The Beach of Falesá' and 'The Ebb-Tide', both of which explore the same moral terrain as *Dr. Jekyll and Mr. Hyde.*

431179 304pp £2.50

Weir of Hermiston

Edited with an introduction by Karl Miller

Set in Edinburgh at the end of the eighteenth century, *Weir of Hermiston* is the story of the conflict between Lord Hermiston, a grimly sardonic 'hanging judge', and his idealistic son, Archie, who is banished by his father to a country estate. This edition includes an account of Stevenson's projected conclusion to the novel, left unfinished at the time of his death, as well as passages of draft material.

435603 176pp £4.99

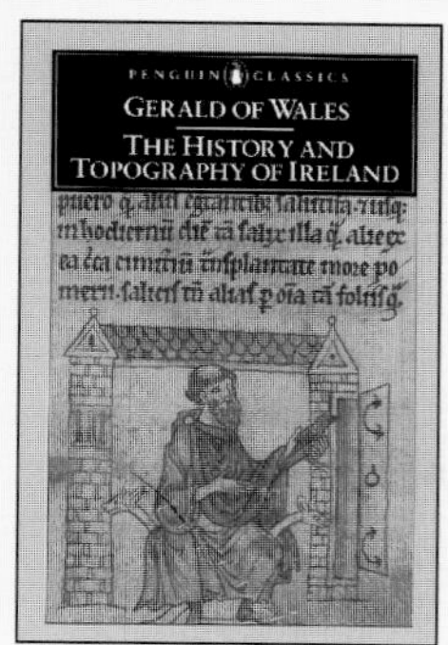

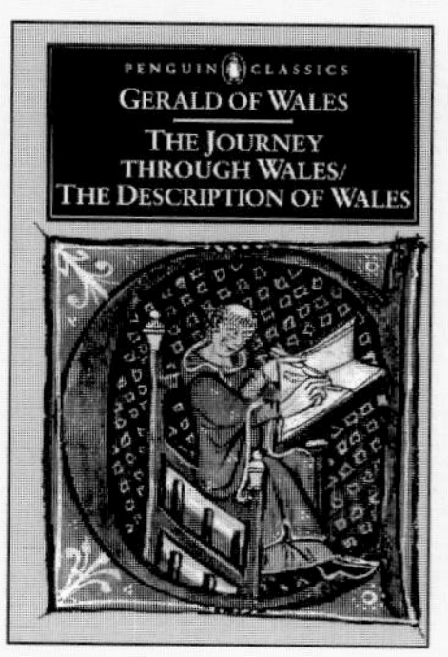

WELSH LITERATURE

GERALD OF WALES

c. 1146–1223

History and Topography of Ireland

Translated with an introduction by
John J O'Meara

Arguably the most authoritative primary source for what is known about medieval Ireland, this lively history by a twelfth-century Norman describes the land's topography, natural resources and inhabitants in vivid detail.

444238 144pp £6.99

The Journey through Wales The Description of Wales

Translated with an introduction by
Lewis Thorpe

The Journey, an accurate and comprehensive history of twelfth-century Wales, is filled with lively anecdotes and folklore; *The Description* offers a fascinating picture of the life of ordinary Welshmen.

443398 336pp £8.99

THE MABINOGION

Translated with an introduction by
Jeffrey Gantz

A combination of fact and fantasy, of myth, history and folklore, *The Mabinogion* conjures up an enchanted world, which is none the less firmly rooted in the forests, hills and valleys of ancient Wales.

443223 320pp £7.99

AMERICAN LITERATURE

HENRY ADAMS

1838-1918

The Education of Henry Adams

Edited with an introduction by Jean Gooder

Adams was a historian, an intellectual born into the fourth generation of a family of distinguished politicians, diplomats and statesmen. In *Education*, he wrote a modernist classic, a brilliant and idiosyncratic blend of autobiography and history.

445579 608pp £9.99

LOUISA M ALCOTT

1832-1888

The Inheritance

Edited with an introduction by Joel Myerson and Daniel Shealy

Written in 1849, when Louisa May Alcott was just seventeen years old, *The Inheritance* is the captivating tale of Edith Adelon, an impoverished Italian orphan who innocently wields the charms of virtue, beauty and loyalty to win her true birthright.

436669 208pp £6.99

Little Women

Introduction by Elaine Showalter with notes by Siobhan Kilfeather and Vinca Showalter

The charming story of the March sisters, *Little Women* has been adored by generations. In this simple, enthralling tale, Louisa May Alcott has created four of American literature's most beloved women.

390693 544pp £6.99

Work

Edited and with an introduction by Joy S Kasson

In this story of a woman's search for a meaningful life, Louisa May Alcott moves outside the family setting of her best-known works. Her concerns about social justice, women's work, domesticity and community lie at the heart of this provocative novel.

39091X 384pp £5.99

EDWARD BELLAMY

1850–1898

Looking Backward 2000–1887

Edited and with an introduction by Cecelia Tichi

It is the year 2000 – and full employment, material abundance and social harmony can be found everywhere.

This is the America to which Julian West, a young Bostonian, awakens after more than a century of sleep. West's initial sense of wonder, his gradual acceptance of the new order and a new love, and Edward Bellamy's wonderful prophetic inventions – electric lighting, shopping malls, credit cards, electronic broadcasting – ensured the mass popularity of this 1888 novel.

390189 240pp £7.99

WILLIAM HILL BROWN AND HANNAH WEBSTER FORSTER

The Power of Sympathy/The Coquette

With an introduction by Carla Mulford

Written in epistolary form and drawn from actual events, *The Power of Sympathy* (1789)

and *The Coquette* (1797) were two of the earliest novels published in America. Both are concerned with the role of women and the prime objective of establishing a secure republic built on the virtue of its citizens.

434682 352pp £8.99

KATE CHOPIN

1850–1904

The Awakening and Selected Stories

Edited with an introduction by Sandra Gilbert

In this daring novel of a woman's sexual and spiritual rebirth, Kate Chopin charts the transformation of a young wife and mother who refuses to be caged by married life and claims for herself moral and erotic freedom. Other selections include 'Emancipation'. 'At the 'Cadian Ball' and 'Desiree's Baby'.

390227 288pp £5.99

JAMES FENIMORE COOPER

1789–1853

The Deerslayer

Introduction by Donald E Pease

Published in 1841, *The Deerslayer*, is the last of the Leatherstocking Tales, which reveal the courageous and persevering nature of the pioneer. Recognized for his descriptive power, James Fenimore Cooper created in Natty Bumppo a mythical character – one of the most significant in American literature.

390618 576pp £6.99

The Last of the Mohicans

Introduction by Richard Slotkin

James Fenimore Cooper's unforgettable portrait of fierce individualism and moral courage is set against the bloody French and Indian War.

390243 384pp £2.50

The Pathfinder

Introduction by Kay Seymour House

A classic account of the American wilderness, *The Pathfinder* continues the adventures of Natty Bumppo, noble woodsman, champion of the Indians and hero of the American frontier.

390715 512pp £6.99

The Pioneers

Introduction and notes by Donald A Ringe

The first of Cooper's renowned Leatherstocking Tales. Quite possibly America's first best-seller, *The Pioneers* today evokes a vibrant and authentic picture of the American pioneering experience.

390073 480pp £5.99

The Prairie

Introduction by Blake Nevius

Infused with imaginative vitality, James Fenimore Cooper's romantic tale of adventure was immediately successful when first published in 1824. It endures as a beautiful reflection of the profound aspirations and disappointments of America's nineteenth-century expansionist movement.

39026X 416pp £5.99

The Spy

Introduction by Wayne Franklin

Set during the American Revolution, *The Spy* is a historical adventure tale reminiscent of Sir Walter Scott's Waverley novels. It is also a parable of the American experience, a reminder that the nation's survival, like its Revolution, depended on judging people by their actions, not their class or reputation.

436286 448pp £7.99

STEPHEN CRANE

1871–1900

The Red Badge of Courage and Other Stories

Edited with an introduction by Pascal Covici Jr

Caught in the nightmare of the American Civil War, a raw Union recruit is finally driven by anger and confusion to a true act of courage. This classic novel about war and its psychological effects is accompanied by five of Stephen Crane's best short stories.

390812 336pp £5.99

FREDERICK DOUGLASS

1817–1895

Narrative of the Life of Frederick Douglass, an American Slave

Edited with an introduction by Houston A Baker Jr

Published in 1845, this autobiography powerfully details the life of the internationally famous abolitionist Frederick Douglass from his birth into slavery in 1818 to his escape to the North in 1838 – how he endured the daily physical and spiritual brutalities of his owners and drivers, how he learned to read and write, and how he grew into a man who could only live free or die.

39012X 160pp £5.99

RALPH WALDO EMERSON

1803–1882

Selected Essays

Edited with an introduction by Larzer Ziff

Ralph Waldo Emerson showed Americans how to be creators of their own circumstances, and turn their backs on Europe's traditional sense of history. These essays brilliantly capture an America discovering her intellectual identity.

390138 416pp £6.99

FANNY FERN

1811–1872

Ruth Hall

Edited with an introduction by Susan Belasco Smith

Writing in 1800s America, Fanny Fern presented a new kind of heroine: a single mother who enjoys a successful career as a journalist, a comfortable income and a formidable bank account. Written as a series of short vignettes and snatches of overheard conversation, *Ruth Hall* is as unconventional in style as in substance and is strikingly modern in impact.

436405 352pp £7.99

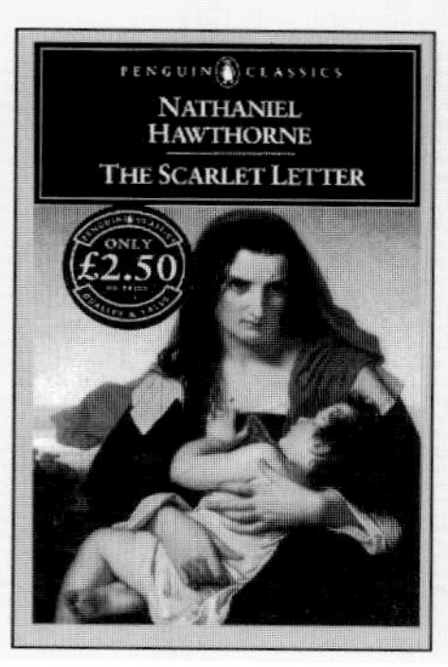

BENJAMIN FRANKLIN

1706–1790

Autobiography and Other Writings

Edited with an introduction by
Kenneth Silverman

Benjamin Franklin was a true Renaissance man and a wholly unconventional human being. The *Autobiography* is an invaluable chronicle of Franklin's rise from a printer's apprentice to an internationally famous scientist, inventor, statesman, legislator and diplomat.

390529 304pp £4.99

NATHANIEL HAWTHORNE

1804–1864

Blithedale Romance

Introduction by Annette Kolodny

In language that is suggestive and often erotic, Nathaniel Hawthorne tells a tale of failed possibilities and multiple personal betrayals as he explores the contrasts between what his characters espouse and what they actually experience in an 'ideal' community.

390286 304pp £5.99

The House of the Seven Gables

Edited with an introduction by
Milton R Stern

Nathaniel Hawthorne's gripping psychological drama about the Pyncheon family, a dynasty founded on pious theft, who live for generations under a dead man's curse until their house is finally exorcised by love.

390057 368pp £5.99

The Marble Faun

Introduction and notes by Richard Brodhead

Nathaniel Hawthorne's novel of Americans abroad is the first novel to explore the influence of European cultural ideas on American morality. It explores how a murder, motivated by love, affects not only the murderer, but also his beloved and their friends.

390774 528pp £6.99

The Scarlet Letter

Introduction by Nina Baym
with notes by Thomas E Connolly

A dramatic, moving depiction of social defiance and social deference, of passion and human frailty. Set in the harsh Puritan community of seventeenth-century Boston, this tale of an adulterous entanglement, that results in an illegitimate birth, reveals Nathaniel Hawthorne's concerns with the tension between the public and the private self. Publicly disgraced, Hester Prynne draws on her inner strength to emerge as the first true heroine of American fiction.

390197 272pp £2.50

The Scarlet Letter and Selected Tales

The Scarlet Letter/The Gray Champion/The Maypole of Merry Mount/The Minister's Black Veil/Young Goodman Brown/The Gentle Boy

Edited by Thomas E Connolly

Nathaniel Hawthorne's greatest novel and some of his best stories, including the inimitable 'Young Goodman Brown'.

430520 384pp £5.99

SELECTED TALES AND SKETCHES

Edited with an introduction by
Michael J Colacurcio

Displaying Hawthorne's understanding of the distinctly American consciousness, these thirty-one short fictions of the early nineteenth-century include 'Young Goodman Brown', 'The Minister's Black Veil' and 'Rappaccini's Daughter'.

39057X 480pp £7.99

THOMAS WENTWORTH HIGGINSON

1823–1911

ARMY LIFE IN A BLACK REGIMENT AND OTHER WRITINGS

Edited with an introduction by R D Madison

This stirring account of wartime experiences from the leader of the first regiment of emancipated slaves 'has some claim to be the best narrative to come from the Union during the Civil War'.

436219 368pp £8.99

WILLIAM DEAN HOWELLS

1837–1920

THE RISE OF SILAS LAPHAM

Edited and with an introduction
by Kermit Vanderbilt

William Dean Howells's richly humorous characterization of a self-made millionaire in Boston society provides a paradigm of American culture in the Gilded Age.

390308 400pp £7.99

GILBERT IMLAY

1754–1828

THE EMIGRANTS

Introduction by Amanda Gilroy and
W M Verhoeven

The Emigrants (1793), one of the first American novels, contrasts the rigid political structures of England with the promise of the American West as a socially just Utopia. Its sensational love plots also dramatize the plight of women trapped in degrading marriages and frankly advocates relaxing divorce laws.

436723 368pp £8.99

NEW JULY 98

HENRY JAMES

1843–1916

THE AMBASSADORS

Edited with an introduction by Harry Levin

The Ambassadors is the finely drawn portrait of a man's late awakening to the importance of morality that is founded not on the dictates of convention but on its intrinsic value.

432337 528pp £5.99

THE AMERICAN

Edited with an introduction by
William Spengemann

Henry James's third novel is an exploration of what became his most powerful and perennial theme – the clash between European and American cultures, the Old World and the New. It is at once a social comedy, a melodramatic romance and a realistic novel of manners.

390820 384pp £5.99

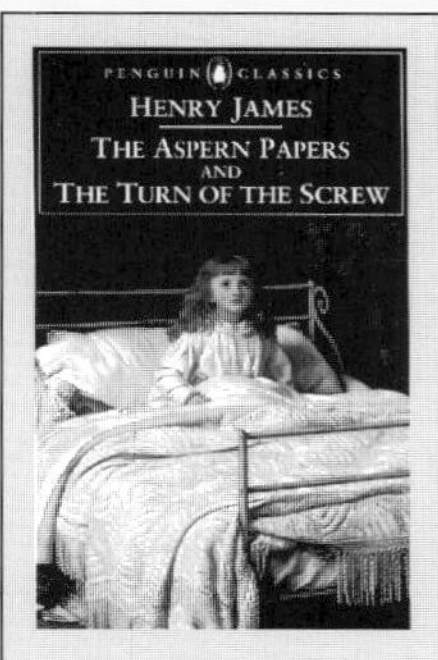

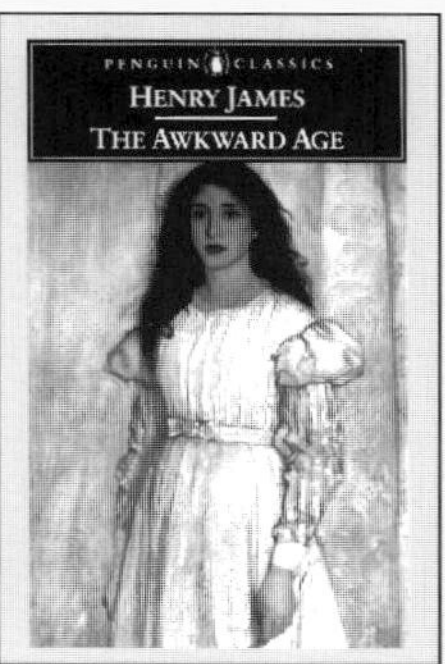

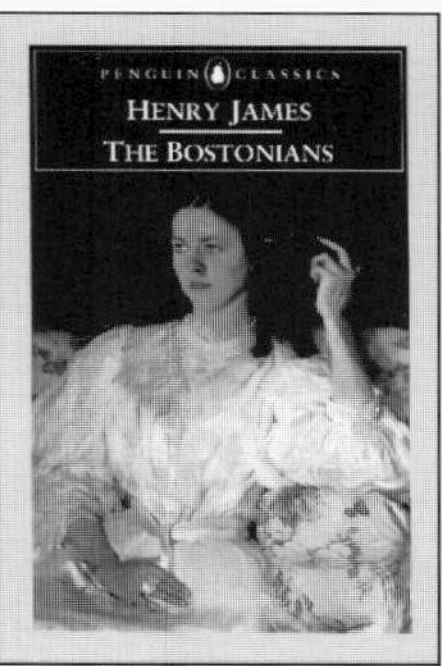

THE AMERICAN SCENE

Edited with an introduction by John F Sears

After living abroad for twenty years, Henry James returned to America and travelled down the East Coast from Boston to Florida. Based on this journey, these writings are at once literary masterpieces, unsurpassed guidebooks, and penetrating reflections of the international themes in his fiction.

43416X 328pp £6.99

THE ASPERN PAPERS THE TURN OF THE SCREW

Edited with an introduction by Anthony Curtis

These two tales reveal at its finest James's genius for creating a world out of a single incident and charging it with unforgettable dramatic tension.

432248 272pp £2.50

THE AWKWARD AGE

Edited by Ronald Blythe with notes by Patricia Crick

Nanda Brookenham is 'coming out' in London society. Thrust suddenly into the immoral circle that has gathered round her mother, she finds herself in competition with Mrs Brookenham for the affection of the man she admires. *The Awkward Age* is a brilliant study of innocence exposed to corrupting influences.

432973 352pp £5.99

THE BOSTONIANS

Edited with an introduction by Charles Anderson

The story of a Mississippi lawyer, a radical feminist, and their struggle for exclusive possession of the beautiful Verena Tarrant has attracted virtually as much controversy as it has readers. In the glitter and moral illumination of its comedy, *The Bostonians* ranks with Henry James's greatest novels in its portrayal of what it means to be fully human.

432256 448pp £2.99

THE CRITICAL MUSE

Selected Literary Criticism

Edited with an introduction by Roger Gard

This volume includes generous selections from James's writings on individual authors (Flaubert, Turgenev, Hawthorne, Balzac and George Eliot among others) as well as from his prefaces and from the general essays which have been so enormously influential in shaping twentieth-century views of literature.

432701 640pp £9.99

DAISY MILLER

Edited with an introduction by Geoffrey Moore with notes by Patricia Crick

Daisy Miller (1878) was James's first really popular novel and the first of his great portraits of the American female.

432620 128pp £1.99

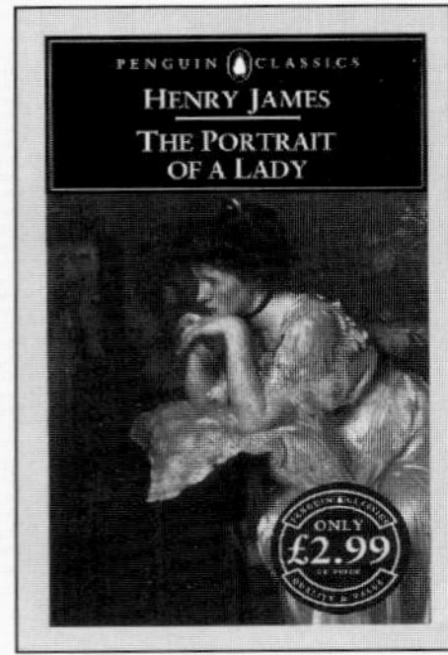

The Europeans

Edited with an introduction by Tony Tanner with notes by Patricia Crick

Set in the countryside around Boston in the mid-nineteenth century, *The Europeans* is concerned with the effect of Old World experience on New World innocence.

432329 208pp £2.50

The Figure in the Carpet and Other Stories

Edited with an introduction by Frank Kermode

This collection of stories of the literary life bears out Henry James's famous assertion that 'Art makes life, makes interest, makes importance...' Several are elaborate Jamesian games, and all are concerned with the art of fiction and the position of the artist in society.

432558 464pp £7.99

The Golden Bowl

Introduction by Gore Vidal with notes by Patricia Crick

The novel opens with Prince Amerigo musing in Bond Street on his approaching marriage, and on the likely consequences of an alliance between Roman aristocracy and American millions.

'The Golden Bowl is a work unique among all his novels: it is James's only novel in which things come out right for his characters...' Leon Edel in *The Life of Henry James*

432353 592pp £5.99

Italian Hours

Edited with an introduction by John Auchard

In these essays on travels in Italy written from 1872 to 1909, Henry James explores art and religion, political shifts and cultural revolutions, and the nature of travel itself.

435077 416pp £7.99

The Jolly Corner and Other Tales

Edited with an introduction by Roger Gard

'A substantial taste of James's distinctive art in its latest flower.' These amusing and eloquent short stories, composed after 1900, explore the sense of unfulfilment and dangerous contingency that may come with age. Having withdrawn from the metropolitan glitter to his house in Rye, Henry James examines the potency of missed possibilities and the shock of the new brash civilization emerging in his native America.

433287 320pp £6.99

The Portrait of a Lady

Edited with an introduction by Geoffrey Moore and with notes by Patricia Crick

An American heiress newly arrived in Europe, Isabel Archer grows into one of Henry James's most magnificent heroines. She does not look to a man to furnish her with her destiny; instead she desires, with grace and courage, to find it herself.

43223X 656pp £2.99

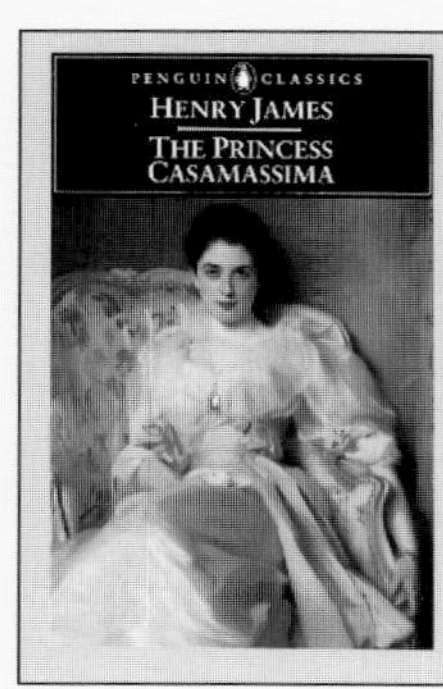

THE PRINCESS CASAMASSIMA

Edited with an introduction by Derek Brewer with notes by Patricia Crick

One of Henry James's most personal novels, *The Princess Casamassima* should 'be read by anyone interested in the contrasts between wealth and poverty, fineness of spirit and vulgarity, terrorism and beauty, as they attract and afflict our feelings. It is as relevant today as when it was first published in 1886.' from the introduction

43254X 608pp £8.99

RODERICK HUDSON

Edited with an introduction by Geoffrey Moore with notes by Patricia Crick

In his first full-length novel James writes with verve and passion about an egotistical young sculptor and the mentor who tries to help him develop his talents.

432647 400pp £5.99

THE SACRED FOUNT

Edited with an introduction by John Lyon

The Sacred Fount is a fascinatingly complex read in which the narrator begins to research and elaborate an intriguing theory of relationships. 'It is perhaps the most audacious move in James's varied and audacious writing.' from the introduction

433503 240pp £5.99

THE SPOILS OF POYNTON

Edited with an introduction by David Lodge and with notes by Patricia Crick

Mrs Gereth is convinced that dreamy, highly strung Fleda Vetch would make the perfect daughter-in-law. But her son has engaged himself to be married to the embarrassingly nouveau philistine Mona Brigstock. Henry James is at his most subtle as the dramatic family quarrel unfolds.

432884 256pp £5.99

THE TRAGIC MUSE

Edited with an introduction by Philip Horne

A young Englishman courageously resists the glittering parliamentary career desired for him by his family, in order to paint. This conflict between art and 'the world' is brilliantly evoked during the course of the novel.

433899 576pp £9.99

WASHINGTON SQUARE

Edited with an introduction by Brian Lee

Washington Square (1880), set in New York, is a spare and intensely moving story of divided loyalties and innocence betrayed. Graham Greene has hailed it as 'perhaps the only novel in which a man has successfully invaded the feminine field and produced a work comparable to Jane Austen's.'

432264 224pp £1.99

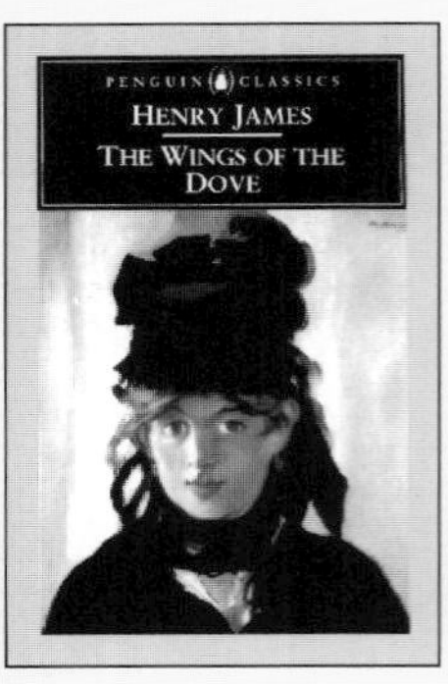

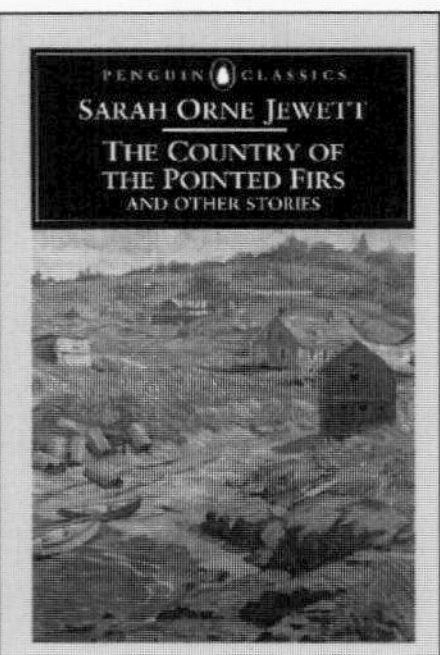

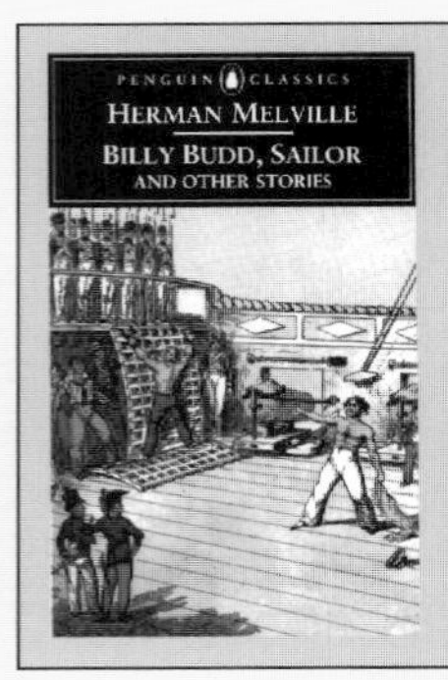

WHAT MAISIE KNEW

Edited with an introduction by Paul Theroux with notes by Patricia Crick

Shuttled between divorced parents who value her only as a means for provoking each other, Maisie grows up in a world of distasteful adult intrigue. Yet her spirit remains unspoilt; and Henry James's great achievement is to project, through his young heroine, a light which she herself is too innocent to understand, but which lends subtle irony to the actions of her corrupt adult companions.

432485 288pp £3.99

THE WINGS OF THE DOVE

Edited with an introduction by John Bayley with notes by Patricia Crick

Human greed and human tragedy are the themes of this beautifully worked novel which, with *The Ambassadors* and *The Golden Bowl*, marks, as John Bayley comments, 'the crown of Henry James's achievement'.

432639 528pp £5.99

WILLIAM JAMES

1842–1910

VARIETIES OF RELIGIOUS EXPERIENCE

Edited with an introduction by Martin E Harty

William James believed that individual religious experiences, rather than the precepts of organized religions, were the backbone of the world's religious life. His discussions of conversion, repentance, mysticism and saintliness, and his observations on actual, personal religious experiences, all support this thesis.

390340 576pp £7.99

SARAH ORNE JEWETT

1849–1909

THE COUNTRY OF THE POINTED FIRS AND OTHER STORIES

Edited with an introduction by Alison Easton

Composed in a series of beautiful web-like sketches, the novel is narrated by a young woman writer who unfolds a New England idyll rooted in friendship, particularly female friendship, weaving stories and conversations and imagery of sea, sky and earth, into a historically significant 'fiction of community'. This edition also includes ten of Sarah Orne Jewett's short stories, among them 'The Queen's Twin', 'The Foreigner' and 'William's Wedding'.

434763 304pp £7.99

JAMES MADISON, ALEXANDER HAMILTON AND JOHN JAY

THE FEDERALIST PAPERS

Edited with an introduction by Isaac Kramnick

The definitive exposition of the American Constitution, *The Federalist Papers* (1787–8) were considered by Thomas Jefferson to be 'the best commentary on the principles of government which ever was written'.

444955 528pp £9.99

HERMAN MELVILLE

1819–1891

BILLY BUDD, SAILOR AND OTHER STORIES

Edited with an introduction by Harold Beaver

The tales in this selection of Melville's shorter fiction are products of the strange and complex imagination that produced *Moby-Dick*.

430296 464pp £5.99

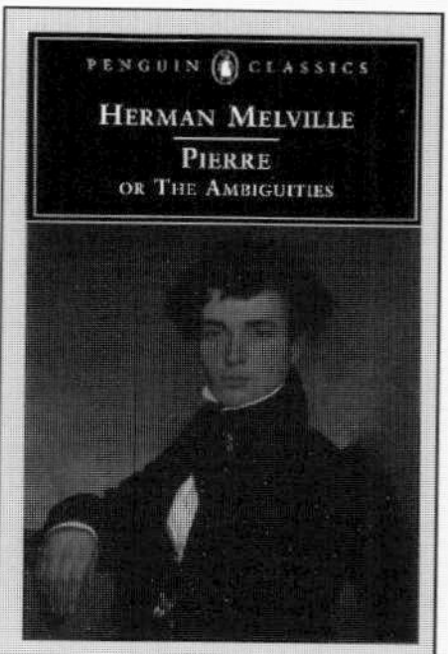

THE CONFIDENCE-MAN

Edited with an introduction by
Stephen Matterson

Part satire, part allegory, part hoax, *The Confidence-Man* is a slippery metaphysical comedy set on April Fool's Day aboard the Mississippi steamer *Fidele*.

445471 400pp £6.99

MOBY-DICK, OR THE WHALE

Edited with an introduction by Andrew Delbanco and explanatory commentary by Tom Quirk

Moby-Dick is the story of an eerily compelling madman pursuing an unholy war against a creature as vast and dangerous and unknowable as the sea itself. Written with wonderfully redemptive humour, it is also a profound inquiry into character, faith and the nature of perception.

390847 720pp £2.99

PIERRE, OR THE AMBIGUITIES

Edited with an introduction by
William C Spengemann

Although it was considered 'a dead failure' on publication in 1852, latter-day critics have recognized in the story of Melville's idealistic young hero a corrosive satire of the sentimental-Gothic novel, and a revolutionary foray into modernist literary techniques.

434844 416pp £7.99

REDBURN

Edited with an introduction by Harold Beaver

From his own experiences as a 'boy' on a packet ship sailing between New York and Liverpool, Melville wove the story of Wellingborough Redburn: a tale of pastoral innocence transformed into disenchantment and disillusionment.

431055 448pp £7.99

TYPEE

Edited with an introduction by
George Woodcock

Typee is a fast-moving adventure tale, an autobiographical account of the author's Polynesian stay, an examination of the nature of good and evil and a frank exploration of sensuality and exotic ritual.

430709 368pp £6.99

FRANCIS PARKMAN

1823–1893

THE OREGON TRAIL

Edited and with an introduction by
David Levin

The Oregon Trail exuberantly documents Francis Parkman's 1846 expedition into the American wilderness. Observed with a reporter's eye and recorded in detail, the whole panorama of life on the Great Plains comes forth against the cruel indifference and majesty of the vast land itself.

390421 464pp £7.99

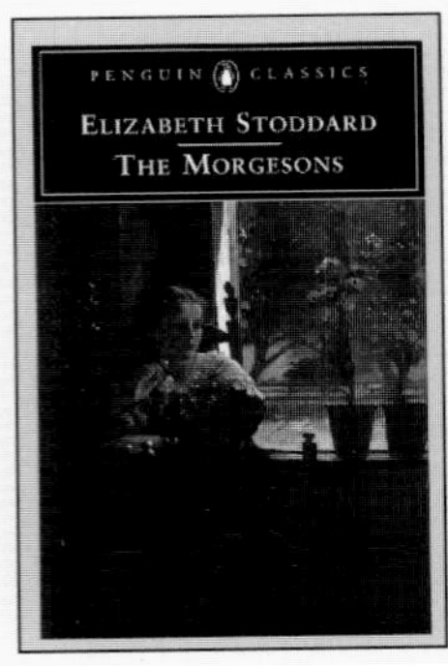

EDGAR ALLAN POE

1809–1849

Comedies and Satires

Edited with an introduction by David Galloway

Edgar Allan Poe did not restrict his abundant imagination to tales of horror and suspense. The writings in this volume, on the contrary, testify to a comic vision derived from a keen sense of literary absurdities and pretensions.

390553 256pp £6.99

The Fall of the House of Usher and Other Writings

Edited with an introduction by David Galloway

This collection reveals Edgar Allan Poe as the arch-priest of Gothic horror. Generous selections from his poetry and critical writings also reveal him as the most exotic of American writers, whose investigations of extreme states of consciousness have a particular relevance today. Originally published under the title *Selected Writings*.

432914 544pp £2.50

The Narrative of Arthur Gordon Pym of Nantucket

Edited with an introduction by Harold Beaver

Set in 1827, this is an exciting blend of romantic adventure and realistic detail. The young hero becomes a stowaway on board an American brig and finds himself in the midst of mutiny, shipwreck and famine.

430970 320pp £5.99

The Science Fiction of Edgar Allan Poe

Edited with an introduction and commentary by Harold Beaver

The sixteen stories in this volume, including the celebrated *Eureka*, reveal Poe as both apocalyptic prophet and pioneer of science fiction.

431063 464pp £6.99

JACOB A RIIS

1849–1914

How the Other Half Lives

With an introduction by Luc Sante

Published in 1890, Jacob Riis's remarkable study of the horrendous living conditions of the poor in New York City had an immediate and extraordinary impact on society, inspiring reforms that affected the lives of millions of people. Riis's reliance on hard facts as the weapons of social criticism pioneered the style of crusading journalism that continues today. His use of photographs (reproduced in this edition) to put faces to his stories was a landmark in photojournalism.

436790 256pp £8.99

ELIZABETH STODDARD

1823–1902

The Morgesons

With an introduction by Lawrence Buell and Sandra A Zagarell

Elizabeth Stoddard's revolutionary novel, written in 1862, explores the conflict between a woman's instinct, passion and will, and the social taboos, family allegiances and tradition-

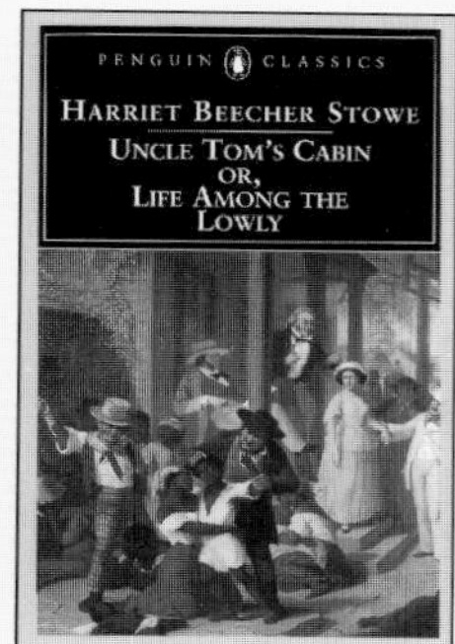

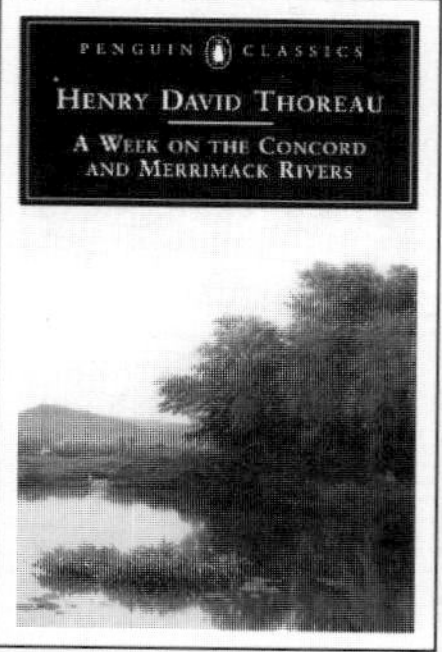

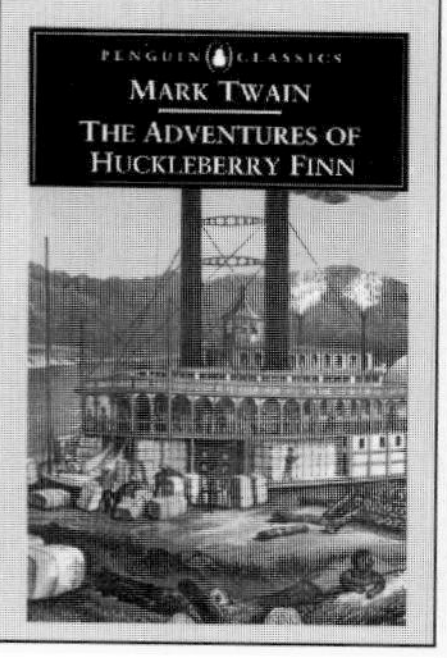

al New England restraint that inhibit her. 'Stoddard was, next to Melville and Hawthorne, the most strikingly original voice in the mid-nineteenth-century American novel.' from the introduction

436510 304pp £7.99

HARRIET BEECHER STOWE

1811–1896

UNCLE TOM'S CABIN

Edited with an introduction by Ann Douglas

Perhaps the most powerful document in the history of American abolitionism, this controversial novel goaded thousands of readers to take a stand on the issue of slavery and played a major political and social role in the Civil War period.

390030 640pp £6.99

HENRY DAVID THOREAU

1817–1862

WALDEN *AND* CIVIL DISOBEDIENCE

Introduction by Michael Meyer

Disdainful of America's growing commercialism and industrialism, Henry David Thoreau left Concord, Massachusetts, in 1845 to live in solitude in the woods by Walden Pond. *Walden*, the classic account of his stay there, conveys at once a naturalist's wonder at the commonplace and a Transcendentalist's yearning for spiritual truth and self-reliance. *Civil Disobedience* is perhaps the most famous essay in American literature – and the inspiration for social activists around the world, from Gandhi to Martin Luther King, Jr.

390448 432pp £5.99

WEEK ON THE CONCORD AND MERRIMACK RIVERS

Edited with an introduction by H Daniel Peck

Thoreau's account of his 1839 boat trip is a finely crafted tapestry of travel writing, essays and lyrical poetry. Day-by-day descriptions of natural phenomena and local characters are interwoven with digressions on literature, religion and philosophy.

434429 368pp £7.99

NEW MAY 99

MARK TWAIN

1835–1910

THE ADVENTURES OF HUCKLEBERRY FINN 

Edited with an introduction by Peter Coveney

'All modern American literature comes from one book by Mark Twain called *Huckleberry Finn* ... There was nothing before. There has been nothing as good since.' Hemingway's comment is scarcely an exaggeration. While critics have argued over the symbolic significance of Huck's and Jim's voyage down the Mississippi, none has disputed the greatness of the book itself.

430180 400pp £1.99

THE ADVENTURES OF TOM SAWYER

Introduction by John Seelye

Tom Sawyer is Mark Twain's hymn to the secure and fantastic world of boyhood and adventure. But beneath the innocence of childhood lie the inequities of adult reality – base emotions and superstitions, murder and revenge, starvation and slavery.

390480 256pp £2.50

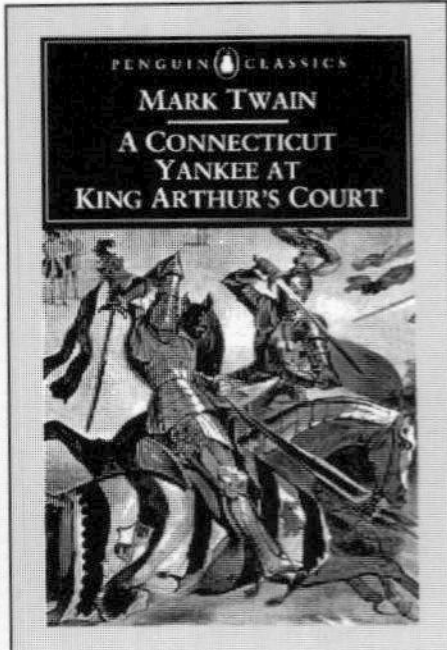

A CONNECTICUT YANKEE AT KING ARTHUR'S COURT

Edited with an introduction by Justin Kaplan

A mechanic from Hartford, Connecticut, wakes up to find himself in sixth-century England. Mark Twain chronicles the results – satiric, satanic, anguished and anarchic – of an imaginary confrontation between the new, nineteenth-century America and Old England.

430644 416pp £6.99

LIFE ON THE MISSISSIPPI

Introduction by James M Cox

In 1882 Mark Twain returned to the river of his childhood, determined to write the definitive travel book on the Mississippi. The result is a wonderful collection of lively anecdotes, tall tales and character sketches; historical facts and information; and reminiscences of the author's boyhood and experiences as a steamboat pilot.

390502 448pp £5.99

THE PRINCE AND THE PAUPER

Introduction by Jerry Griswold

First published in 1881, *The Prince and the Pauper* is the story of a poor boy, Tom Canty, who exchanges clothes and identities with Edward Tudor, the prince of England. With characteristic humour and colour, Mark Twain brings to life the sixteenth-century royal court, the crowded, boisterous streets inhabited by London's hoi polloi and the behaviour of two young boys who are in many ways smarter than their elders.

436693 256pp £5.99

PUDD'NHEAD WILSON

Edited with an introduction by Malcolm Bradbury

In *Pudd'nhead Wilson*, Mark Twain returns to the idyllic river community of his childhood. He uses certain stock characters and devices, such as the sardonic cracker-barrel philosopher, the scoundrel unmasked, and the substitution of babies, to build up a complex, ironical and morally disturbing account of human nature under slavery.

430407 320pp £5.99

ROUGHING IT

Edited with an introduction by Hamlin Hill

Mark Twain's ramblings took him all over the American West during the 1860s. He prospected for gold and silver, speculated on timber and mining stocks, sailed to Hawaii and worked for a succession of small newspapers. *Roughing It* is his fictionalized account of these years.

390103 592pp £6.99

SHORT STORIES

Edited with an introduction by Justin Kaplan

'The humorous story is strictly a work of art – high and delicate art – and only an artist can tell it.' Mark Twain in 'How to Tell a Story'

This volume collects together sixty-five of the best of Mark Twain's short stories. It includes ghost stories and detective stories, fables and fairy tales, domestic comedies, hoaxes, social satire and sketches.

433848 688pp £8.99

TALES, SPEECHES, ESSAYS AND SKETCHES

Edited with an introduction by Tom Quirk

Masterful short fiction and prose pieces display the variety of Twain's imaginative invention, his diverse talents, and his extraordinary emotional range. The volume includes 'Jim Smiley and His Jumping Frogs', 'The Man that Corrupted Hadleyberg', 'Fenimore Cooper's Literary Offenses' and the spectacularly scatalogical 'Date, 1601'.

434178 448pp £7.99

A TRAMP ABROAD

Introduction by Hamlin Hill and Robert Gray Bruce

Twain's account of travelling in Europe sparkles with the author's shrewd observations and highly opinionated comments on Old World culture, and showcases his unparalleled ability to integrate humorous sketches, autobiographical tidbits and historical anecdotes in a consistently entertaining narrative.

436081 448pp £7.99

BOOKER T WASHINGTON

1856–1915

UP FROM SLAVERY

Introduction by Louis R Harlan

During his unchallenged reign as black America's foremost spokesman, former slave Booker T Washington trod a dangerous middle ground in a time of racial backlash and disfranchisement. Vividly recounting his life – his childhood as a slave, his struggle for education, his founding and presidency of the Tuskegee Institute, his meetings with the country's leaders – *Up From Slavery* reveals the conviction he held that the black man's salvation lay in education, industriousness and self-reliance.

390510 400pp £6.99

WALT WHITMAN

1819–1892

THE COMPLETE POEMS

Edited with an introduction by Francis Murphy

'This is the unrestful, ungraspable poetry of the sheer present ... Whitman's is the best poetry of this kind' D H Lawrence

422226 896pp £12.50

LEAVES OF GRASS

The First 1855 edition

Edited with an introduction by Malcolm Cowley

This is the original and complete 1855 edition of one of the greatest masterpieces of American literature, including Whitman's own introduction to the work.

421998 192pp £5.99

AMERICAN LOCAL COLOUR WRITING 1880–1920

Edited with an introduction and notes by Elizabeth Ammons and Valerie Rohy

Organized geographically, *American Local Color Writing* features familiar writers such as Kate Chopin, Hamlin Garland, Joel Chandler Harris and Sarah Orne Jewett, and introduces lesser-known voices like Abraham Cahan, Sui Sin Far and Zitkala-Sa. The writing sheds light on varying concepts of the 'American Identity': the African-American experience; shifting notions of gender and sexuality; and radical, class and ethnic stereotypes.

43688X 480pp £9.99

NEW JUNE 98

EARLY AMERICAN DRAMA

Edited with an introduction and notes by Jeffrey H. Richards

This unique volume includes eight dramas that mirror American literary, social and cultural history: Royall Tyler's *The Contrast* (1787), Robert Montgomery Bird's *The Gladiator* (1831); William Dunlap's *André* (1798); James Nelson Barker's *The Indian Princess* (1808); William Henry Smith's *The Drunkard* (1844); Anna Cora Mowatt's *Fashion* (1845); George L Aiken's 1852 dramatization of *Uncle Tom's Cabin*; and Dion Boucicault's *The Octoroon* (1859).

435883 560pp £9.99

FOUR STORIES BY AMERICAN WOMEN

Rebecca Harding Davis/Life in the Iron Mills

Charlotte Perkins Gilman/The Yellow Wallpaper

Sarah Orne Jewett/The Country of the Pointed Firs

Edith Wharton/Souls Belated

Notes by Sarah Higginson Begley and M Kearney

Representing four prominent women writers who flourished in the period following the Civil War, these masterpieces of short fiction helped blaze a trail for the recognition and acceptance of women in the literary world.

390766 272pp £6.99

WOMEN'S INDIAN CAPTIVITY NARRATIVES

Edited with an introduction and notes by Kathryn Derounian-Stodola

The narrative of capture by Native Americans is arguably the first American literary form dominated by the experiences of women. For this pioneering collection, Kathryn Derounian-Stodola has selected ten extraordinary tales that span over two hundred years (1682–1892) and show geographical as well as literary diversity.

436715 400pp £8.99

NEW MAY 99

EUROPEAN LANGUAGE

LITERATURE

Courtesy of Giraudon

DUTCH LITERATURE

ERASMUS OF ROTTERDAM

1467–1536

Praise of Folly
Letter to Maarten van Dorp

Translated by Betty Radice
Introduction and notes by A H T Levi

The best introduction to the work of Erasmus, this is one of the finest masterpieces of the sixteenth century, updated and superbly translated to reflect the latest scholarly research.

446087 256pp £7.99

MULTATULI

1820–1887

Max Havelaar or The Coffee Auctions of a Dutch Trading Company

Translated by Roy Edwards
with an introduction by R P Meijer

Based on the author's actual experiences, *Max Havelaar* is one of the most forceful indictments of colonialism ever written. Its portrayal of colonial cruelty in Indonesia is rendered in prose that ranges from colloquial informality to cadences of biblical resonance, and the sophistication of its satire led D H Lawrence to compare it to the works of Swift, Gogol and Twain.

445161 352pp £8.99

BENEDICT DE SPINOZA

1632–1677

Ethics

Translated by Edwin Curley with an introduction by Stuart Hampshire

Using a strict step-by-step logical format, *Ethics* examines the natural order of the world, the place of human beings within it, the distinction between bodies and minds, and the consequences for our happiness and freedom. It argues that we can all learn to become 'passionately reasonable', by re-directing our emotions towards conciliation and the enjoyment of living.

435719 208pp £6.99

VINCENT VAN GOGH

1853–1890

The Letters of Vincent Van Gogh

Selected and edited by Ronald De Leeuw

Translated by Arnold Pomerans

This new selection of Van Gogh's letters, based on an entirely new translation, reinstates a large number of passages omitted from earlier editions. It contains complete letters wherever possible, linked with brief passages of connecting narrative, expressly designed to demonstrate Van Gogh's inner journey as well as the outward facts of his life. 'If ever there was any doubt that Van Gogh's letters belong beside those great classics of artistic self-revelation, Cellini's autobiography and Delacroix's journal, this excellent new edition dispels it.' *The Times*

446745 560pp £11.99

FRENCH LITERATURE

HONORÉ DE BALZAC

1799–1850

The Black Sheep

Translated with an introduction by
Donald Adamson

Two Brothers – one a dashing, handsome ex-soldier, the other a sensitive artist – struggle to recover the family inheritance in a novel that explores the devastation that poverty can bring.

442375 352pp £7.99

César Birotteau

Translated with an introduction by
Robin Buss

In this powerful novel about business, the petite bourgeoisie, and human failure – set in 1819, at the dawn of the new age of capitalism – Balzac pioneered a new genre: the tragedy of the little man.

446419 320pp £6.99

The Chouans

Translated with an introduction by
Marion Ayton Crawford

The first volume in Balzac's lifework, comprehensively entitled *The Human Comedy*, this tale of a Royalist uprising against the post-revolutionary republic is rendered with characteristic passion and mastery of detail.

44260X 400pp £7.99

Cousin Bette

Translated with an introduction by
Marion Ayton Crawford

Vividly bringing to life the rift between the old world and the new, *Cousin Bette* is an incisive study of vengeance, and the culmination of *The Human Comedy*.

441603 448pp £5.99

Cousin Pons

Translated with an introduction by
Herbert J Hunt

The companion novel to *Cousin Bette*, *Cousin Pons* offers a diametrically opposite view of the nature of family relationships, focusing on a mild, harmless old man.

442057 336pp £8.99

Eugenie Grandet

Translated with an introduction by
Marion Ayton Crawford

The love of money and the passionate pursuit of it, a major theme in *The Human Comedy*, is brilliantly depicted in the story of Grandet and his obsession with achieving power.

44050X 256pp £5.99

A Harlot High and Low

Translated with an introduction by
Rayner Heppenstall

Finance, fashionable society, and the intrigues of the underworld and the police system form the heart of this powerful novel, which introduces the satanic genius Vautrin, one of the greatest villains in world literature.

442324 560pp £7.99

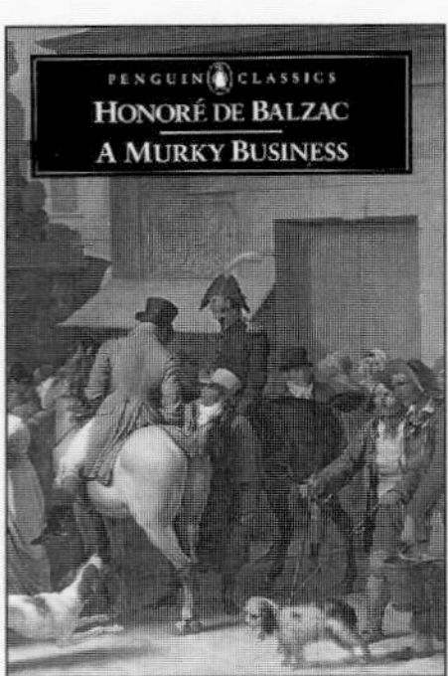

History of the Thirteen

Translated with an introduction by Herbert J Hunt

This trilogy of stories – 'Ferragus: Chief of the Companions of Duty', 'The Duchesse De Langeais' and 'The Girl with the Golden Eyes' – purporting to be the history of a secret society, laid the foundation for Balzac's *Scenes of Parisian Life* and is a stunning evocation of all ranks of society.

443010 400pp £7.99

Lost Illusions

Translated with an introduction by Herbert J Hunt

This novel of a young man who is bored with provincial life and tries to make his way in Parisian society is part of *The Human Comedy*.

442510 704pp £7.99

A Murky Business

Translated with an introduction by Herbert J Hunt

Set earlier than most of *The Human Comedy*, this unflinching look at the relationship between political power and morality includes Napoleon, Talleyrand and Fouché as characters.

442715 224pp £6.99

Old Goriot

Translated with an introduction by Marion Ayton Crawford

The intersecting lives of a group of people living in a working-class boarding-house in nineteenth-century Paris form the background of this indictment of the cruelty of city society.

440178 304pp £5.99

Selected Short Stories

Translated with an introduction by Sylvia Raphael

This collection includes 'El Verdugo', 'Domestic Peace', ' A Study in Feminine Psychology', 'An Incident in the Reign of Terror', 'The Conscript', 'The Red Inn', 'The Purse', 'La Grande Bretèche', 'A Tragedy by the Sea', 'The Atheist's Mass', 'Facino Cane' and 'Pierre Grassou'.

443258 272pp £6.99

Ursule Mirouet

Translated with an introduction by Donald Adamson

An essentially simple tale about the struggle and triumph of innocence, this novel also reveals Balzac's lifelong fascination with the occult.

443169 272pp £7.99

The Wild Ass's Skin

Translated with an introduction by Herbert Hunt

Balzac is concerned with the choice between ruthless self-gratification and asceticism, dissipation and restraint, in a novel that is powerful in its symbolism and realistic depiction of decadence.

443304 288pp £6.99

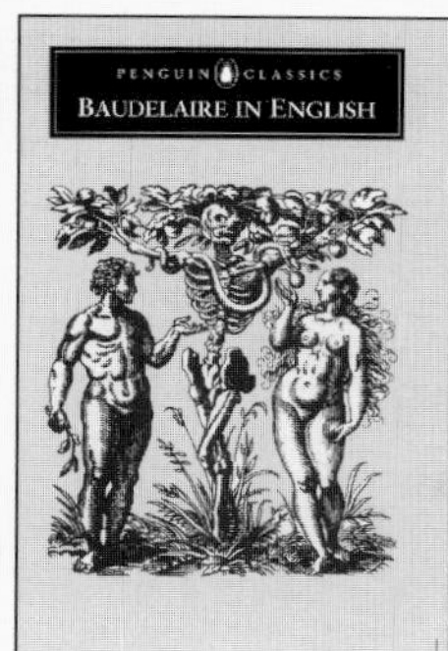

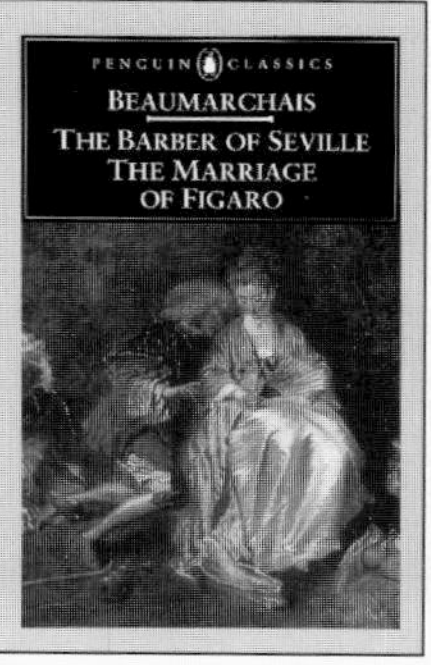

CHARLES BAUDELAIRE

1821–1867

Baudelaire in English

Edited by Carol Clark and Robert Sykes

In his psychological and sexual complexity, images of alienation and fascination with the outcasts of urban life, Charles Baudelaire was a pioneering modern spirit who has proved profoundly influential well beyond the borders of France. This superb anthology brings together the translations of his poetry and 'prose poems' which best reveal the different facets of his personality.

446443 336pp £9.99

Selected Poems

Translated with an introduction by Carol Clark

In both his life and his poetry, Baudelaire pushed the accepted limits of his time. His dissolute bohemian life was as shocking to his nineteenth-century readers as his poetry. Writing in classical style but with brutal honesty, Baudelaire laid bare human suffering, aspirations, and perversions.

446249 272pp £6.99

Selected Writings on Art and Literature

Translated with an introduction by P E Charvet

This collection of criticism by one of the most discerning observers of the nineteenth century also reveals the elegance of expression of one of the greatest poets of France.

446060 464pp £9.99

BEAUMARCHAIS

1732–1799

The Barber of Seville
The Marriage of Figaro

Translated with an introduction by John Wood

Known to us almost exclusively through the operas of Rossini and Mozart, these two plays, written with a delightful light touch, marked high points in eighteenth-century comedy.

441336 224pp £6.99

JEAN-ANTHELME BRILLAT-SAVARIN

1755–1826

The Physiology of Taste

Translated with an introduction by Anne Drayton

Witty, shrewd and anecdotal, containing some of the best recipes for food and some of the most satisfactory observations on life, Brillat-Savarin's book amply proves his own maxim: 'The pleasures of the table belong to all times and all ages, to every country and every day; they go hand in hand with all our other pleasures, outlast them, and remain to console us for their loss.'

446141 384pp £8.99

BENJAMIN CONSTANT

1767–1830

ADOLPHE

Translated with an introduction by Leonard Tancock

Benjamin Constant was for many years the companion of Madame de Staël. It was a stormy affair which often caused him great unhappiness, but he lacked the moral courage to break with her. In *Adolphe*, written in 1816 and known to be largely autobiographical, Constant chronicles just such a love affair.

441344 128pp £5.99

PIERRE CORNEILLE

1616–1684

THE CID
CINNA
THE THEATRICAL ILLUSION

Translated with an introduction by John Cairncross

The Cid, Corneille's masterpiece set in medieval Spain, was the first great work of French classical drama; *Cinna*, written three years later in 1641, is a tense political drama, while *The Theatrical Illusion*, an earlier work, is reminiscent of Shakespeare's exuberant comedies.

443126 288pp £7.99

ALPHONSE DAUDET

1840–1897

LETTERS FROM MY WINDMILL

Translated with an introduction by Frederick Davies

Illustrated by Edward Ardizzone

Throughout his career, celebrated Parisian novelist Daudet remained a true son of Provence. This collection of wryly humorous stories, admired by Flaubert, Dickens and Henry James, evokes the vital rhythms of Provençal life and Daudet's youth in the mid-nineteenth century.

443347 224pp £6.99

RENÉ DESCARTES

1596–1650

DISCOURSE ON METHOD *AND* THE MEDITATIONS

Translated with an introduction by F E Sutcliffe

In these essays published in 1637 and 1641, the father of modern philosophy attacked the prevalent world view and introduced scientific procedure to all fields of human inquiry through application of his methods.

442065 192pp £6.99

MEDITATIONS AND OTHER METAPHYSICAL WRITINGS

Translated with an introduction by Desmond M Clarke

This authoritative new translation is based on the original Latin and French editions of Descartes' principal writings on metaphysics.

447016 272pp £7.99

NEW SEPTEMBER 98

DENIS DIDEROT

1713–1784

Jacques the Fatalist

Translated by Michael Henry with an introduction by Martin Hall

In this revolutionary novel, a leading figure of the Enlightenment celebrates the unpredictable nature of man and the world as he considers the behaviour of the moral being and the philosophical dilemma of free will and determinism.

444726 272pp £6.99

The Nun

Translated by Leonard Tancock

Conventional Christianity is sharply criticized in a tale about a woman confined to a convent against her will.

443002 192pp £6.99

Rameau's Nephew *and* D'Alembert's Dream

Translated with an introduction by Leonard Tancock

In the form of dialogues, Diderot attacks stale conventions and offers a surprisingly modern view of life, sex, and morals.

441735 240pp £6.99

Selected Writings on Art and Literature

Translated with an introduction by Geoffrey Bremner

This collection explores reality and representation in art, literature and theatre in a series of direct, entertaining opinions and dialogues.

445889 400pp £8.99

ALEXANDRE DUMAS

1824–1895

The Count of Monte Cristo

Translated with an introduction by Robin Buss

This magnificent novel of *l'action et l'amour* is set in nineteenth-century metropolitan Paris with interludes in Marseilles and Rome. In it Dumas gave free rein to the sensational – hashish-smoking, vampirism and sex – and to his interest in travel, classical myth, the orient, human psychology and disguises.

44615X 1136pp £7.99

The Three Musketeers

Translated with an introduction by Lord Sudley

Based on historic fact, this is the stirring, romantic story of d'Artagnan, Athos, Porthos, and Aramis, and their fight to preserve the honour of their Queen.

440259 720pp £6.99

GUSTAVE FLAUBERT

1821–1880

Bouvard and Pécuchet

Translated with an introduction by A J Krailsheimer

Unfinished at the time of Flaubert's death in 1880, *Bouvard and Pécuchet* features two Chaplinesque figures in a farce that mocks bourgeois stupidity and the banality of intellectual life in France.

443207 336pp £7.99

Flaubert in Egypt

Translated with an introduction by
Francis Steegmuller

Flaubert in Egypt wonderfully captures the young writer's impressions during his 1849 voyages. Using diaries, letters, travel notes, and the evidence of Flaubert's travelling companion, Maxine Du Camp, Francis Steegmuller reconstructs his journey through the bazaars and brothels of Cairo and down the Nile to the Red Sea.

435824 240pp £6.99

Madame Bovary

Translated with an introduction
by Geoffrey Wall

Flaubert's landmark story unfolds the desperate love affair of Emma Bovary, the bored provincial housewife who abandons her husband in defiance of bourgeois values.

445269 320pp £2.50

Salammbo

Translated with an introduction by
A J Krailsheimer

An epic story of lust, cruelty, and sensuality, this historical novel is set in Carthage in the days of following the First Punic War with Rome.

443282 288pp £6.99

Selected Letters

Translated with an introduction
by Geoffrey Wall

'The spontaneous eloquence of these letters, their special heady compound of fantasy, laughter and critical intelligence ... They take their place alongside Coleridge's journals, Henry James's notebooks, Virginia Woolf's diaries and the *cahiers* of Paul Valèry.'
Geoffrey Wall

446079 496pp £9.99

Sentimental Education

Translated with an introduction by
Robert Baldick

Flaubert skilfully re-creates the fibre of his times and society in this novel of a young man's romantic attachment to an older woman.

441417 432pp £5.99

The Temptation of St Antony

Translated with an introduction by
Kitty Mrosovsky

One of Flaubert's earliest works, this prose poem is a series of visions and arguments quite different in mood and style from his other writings.

444106 304pp £6.99

Three Tales

Translated with an introduction by
Robert Baldick

In *A Simple Life*, Flaubert recounts the life of a pious servant girl; in *The Legend of St Julian*, Hospitaller gives insight into medieval mysticism; and *Hérodias* is a powerful story of the martyrdom of St John the Baptist.

441069 128pp £4.99

FRENCH POETRY 1820–1950

Edited with an introduction by William Rees

While this anthology contains, of course, generous selections from the established giants – Baudelaire, Rimbaud, Mallarmé, Valéry, Apollinaire, Michaux – it also draws attention to interesting 'minor' poets, such as Claudel or Cendrars, whose writing has been vital to the evolution of poetry in France.

423850 896pp £15.99

JEAN FROISSART

c. 1337–1410

CHRONICLES

Translated with an introduction by Geoffrey Brereton

This selection from Froissart's *Chronicles* forms a vast panorama of Europe, from the deposition of Edward II to the downfall of Richard II.

442006 496pp £9.99

GREGORY OF TOURS

c. 540–594

THE HISTORY OF THE FRANKS

Translated with an introduction by Lewis Thorpe

This colourful narrative of French history in the sixth century is a dramatic and detailed portrait of a period of political and religious turmoil.

442952 720pp £12.00

FRANÇOIS GUIZOT

1787–1874

A HISTORY OF CIVILIZATION IN EUROPE

Translated by William Hazlitt

Edited with an introduction by L Siedentop

In a work that stresses the role of class conflict as a catalyst for social change, Guizot shows how urban growth and a market economy led to the dominance of the bourgeoisie and the creation of a democratic, capitalist society acknowledging detrimental effects on local autonomy.

446656 304pp £8.99

VICTOR HUGO

1802–1885

LES MISÉRABLES

Translated with an introduction by Norman Denny

Including unforgettable descriptions of the Paris sewers, the Battle of Waterloo, and the fighting at the barricades during the July Revolution, this is at once a thrilling narrative and a vivid social document.

444300 1232pp £7.99

NOTRE-DAME DE PARIS

Translated with an introduction by John Sturrock

Hugo's powerful evocation of Paris in 1482 and the tragic tale of Quasimodo, the hunchback of Notre-Dame, has become a classic example of French romanticism.

443533 496pp £6.99

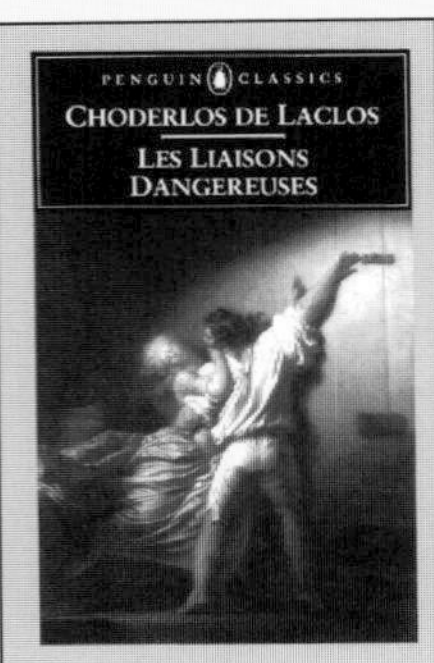

JORIS-KARL HUYSMANS

1848–1907

Against Nature

Translated by Robert Baldick

This chronicle of the exotic practices and perverse pleasures of a hero, who is a thinly disguised version of the author, was condemned by the public as a work of alarming depravity – and was much admired by Oscar Wilde.

440860 224pp £6.99

JOINVILLE AND VILLEHARDOUIN

b. 1224 1150–1218

Chronicles of the Crusades

Translated with an introduction by M R B Shaw

These two famous Old French chronicles were composed by soldiers who took part in the Holy Wars and offer both eyewitness accounts of the battles and pictures of life in the East.

441247 368pp £8.99

LA FONTAINE

1621–1695

Selected Fables

Translated by James Michie with an introduction by Geoffrey Grigson

Although he drew from Aesop, Phaedrus, and the Persians, La Fontaine reinvented the fable in verses full of irresistible freshness.

443762 176pp £6.99

LA ROCHEFOUCAULD

1613–1680

Maxims

Translated with an introduction by Leonard Tancock

The philosophy of La Rochefoucauld, which influenced French intellectuals as diverse as Voltaire and the Jansenists, is captured here in more than 600 penetrating and pithy aphorisms.

44095X 128pp £5.99

PIERRE CHODERLOS DE LACLOS

1741–1803

Les Liaisons Dangereuses

Translated with an introduction by P W K Stone

One of the most notorious novels of all time, this eighteenth-century work describes the intrigues of a depraved pair of aristocrats plotting the seduction of a young convent girl.

441166 400pp £6.99

JULES LAFORGUE

1860–1887

Selected Poems

Edited and translated with an introduction by Graham Dunstan Martin

Deeply pessimistic yet full of yearning, tender yet savagely self-mocking, Laforgue has a unique voice and vision which none the less mark him out as one of the founding fathers of modernism.

43626X 352pp £9.99

NEW OCTOBER 98

MADAME DE LAFAYETTE

1634–1693

THE PRINCESS DE CLÈVES

Translated with an introduction by
Robin Buss

This romance about a woman's dangerous but platonic liaison is one of the first feminist novels and a precursor to the psychological realism of Proust.

445870 192pp £6.99

LAUTRÉAMONT

1846–1870

MALDOROR AND POEMS

Translated with an introduction by
Paul Knight

One of the earliest and most astonishing examples of surrealist writing, the hallucinatory tale *Maldoror* was hailed as a work of genius by Gide, Breton, Modigliani and Verlaine. This edition includes a translation of the epigrammatic *Poésies*.

443428 288pp £7.99

MARIE DE FRANCE

c. 1180

THE LAIS OF MARIE DE FRANCE

Translated with an introduction by
Glyn S Burgess and Keith Busby

Twelve short story-poems, based on Breton tales of love in crisis, are presented in plain prose translations as close to the twelfth-century original as possible. The volume includes the Old french text of *Laüstic*.

444769 144pp £6.99

MARGUERITE DE NAVARRE

c. 1580

THE HEPTAMERON

Translated and with an introduction by
P A Chilton

Inspired by a royal project to produce a French *Decameron*, these seventy stories mirroring Renaissance France's version of the battle of the sexes are attributed to Rabelais's patron, the sister of Francis I.

44355X 544pp £9.99

GUY DE MAUPASSANT

1850–1893

BEL-AMI

Translated with an introduction by
Douglas Parmée

In this analysis of power and its corrupting influence, Maupassant captures the sleaziness, manipulation, and mediocrity prevalent in the elegant salons of Paris during the belle epoque.

443150 416pp £6.99

PIERRE AND JEAN

Translated with an introduction by
Leonard Tancock

An intensely personal story of suspicion, jealousy, and family love, this novel shows the influence of such masters as Zola and Flaubert on Maupassant's writings.

443584 176pp £5.99

Selected Short Stories

Translated by Roger Colet with an introduction by Ernest Mandelby

These thirty stories, including 'Boule de Suif', 'Madame Tellier's Establishment', 'The Jewels', 'The Mask', 'A Duel', and 'Mother Savage', range in subject from murder, adultery, and war, to the simple pleasures of eating and drinking.

44243X 368pp £3.50

A Woman's Life

Translated by H N P Sloman with an introduction by Ernest Mandelby

In one of his most popular full-length novels, Maupassant exposes with his characteristic detachment and precision the evil around a woman misused by both her husband and her son.

441611 208pp £6.99

MOLIÈRE

1622–1673

The Misanthrope & Other Plays

Translated with an introduction by John Wood

This collection includes *The Misanthrope*, a drama of unrequited love; *Tartuffe*, the first great comedy of obsession; *The Imaginary Invalid*, a burlesque of doctor-patient relationships; *A Doctor in Spite of Himself*, Molière's most famous farce; and *The Sicilian*.

440895 288pp £5.99

The Miser and Other Plays

Translated with an introduction by John Wood

Molière's classic comedies set the standard for later playwrights. Included here are *The Would-Be Gentleman, The Miser, Don Juan, Love's the Best Doctor,* and *That Scoundrel Scapin.*

440364 288pp £6.99

MICHEL DE MONTAIGNE

1533–1592

An Apology for Raymond Sebond

Translated and edited with an introduction by M A Screech

A masterpiece of Counter-Reformation and Renaissance argument, Montaigne's *Apology* is a witty defence of natural theology and an eloquent expression of Christian scepticism.

444939 240pp £7.99

The Complete Essays

Translated and edited with an introduction and notes by M A Screech

Montaigne, a great sage of Western thought, set out to discover himself in his eclectic collection of essays. What he discovered instead was the nature of the human race, poised at the beginning of the Renaissance. This celebrated translation, in plain contemporary English, is true to his frank style.

446044 1344pp £13.00

THE ESSAYS: A SELECTION

Translated and edited with an introduction and notes by M A Screech

Reflections by the creator of the essay form, display the humane, sceptical, humorous, and honest views of Montaigne, revealing his thoughts on sexuality, religion, cannibals, intellectuals, and other unexpected themes. Included are such celebrated works as 'On Solitude', ' To Philosophize is to Learn How to Die', and 'On Experience'.

446028 480pp £7.99

ESSAYS

Translated with an introduction by J M Cohen

In writing these celebrated essays, Montaigne was creating a new literary form in which he put his own views and opinions on trial. In each piece he set out to discover himself by setting down his reactions and responses to different subjects. In this way he could discern how much of his intellectual standpoint was due to nature, and how much to external forces.

17897X 416pp £7.99

MONTESQUIEU

1689–1755

PERSIAN LETTERS

Translated with an introduction by C J Betts

In the form of letters between two Persian travellers in eighteenth-century Europe, this novel was written to show that France was moving from benevolent monarchy to royal tyranny.

442812 352pp £7.99

GÉRARD DE NERVAL

1808–1855

SELECTED WRITINGS

Edited and translated by Richard Sieburth

Baudelaire regarded de Nerval as the most lucid poet of the age, and Proust ranked him as one of its greatest prose writers. This new Penguin edition offers the most inclusive selection of de Nerval's writings ever to appear in English, covering most of the familiar and fugitive genres in which he excelled: fantastic tales, travel literature, autobiography, essays, literary portraits, sonnets and peregrinations.

44601X 448pp £9.99

NEW JANUARY 99

BLAISE PASCAL

1623–1662

PENSÉES

Translated and with a revised introduction by A J Krailsheimer

This collection of short writings ponders the contrast between man in his fallen state and in a state of grace. It is a work of extraordinary power; a lucid, eloquent and often satirical look at human illusions, self-deceptions and follies.

446451 368pp £7.99

CHRISTINE DE PISAN

b. 1365

The Book of the City of Ladies

Translated with an introduction by
Rosalind Brown-Grant

Christine de Pisan was a pioneer among female authors of the middle ages. *The Book of the City of Ladies* is first and foremost her attempt to defend women from the literary misogyny prevalent at the time.

446893 352pp £8.99

NEW JUNE 99

The Treasure of the City of Ladies or The Book of the Three Virtues

Translated with an introduction by
Sarah Lawson

A valuable counterbalance to most of the rest of our evidence of medieval life which was written by men. Through her writing Christine de Pisan addresses all women, from those at the royal court to prostitutes, painting a vivid picture of their lives in fine detail - and often in a drily amusing way.

44453X 192pp £7.99

ABBÉ PREVOST

1697–1753

Manon Lescaut

Translated by Leonard Tancock with a new introduction by Jean Sgard

Young Chevalier des Grieux's account discloses his love affair with Manon, a femme fatale who makes his life a torment - and without whom it is meaningless.

445595 192pp £6.99

FRANÇOIS RABELAIS

1494–1553

The Histories of Gargantua and Pantagruel

Translated with an introduction by
J M Cohen

Written by a Franciscan monk who was at the centre of the sixteenth-century humanist movement, this robust epic parodies everyone from classic authors to Rabelais's own contemporaries.

44047X 720pp £7.99

RACINE

1639–1699

Andromache/Britannicus/Berenice

Translated with an introduction by
John Cairncross

These three works, which brought Racine acclaim with the public and in the court of Louis XIV, are striking examples of how Racine overturned the theatrical conventions of his time by introducing the force of fate into human drama.

441956 288pp £7.99

Iphigenia/Phaedra/Athaliah

Translated by John Cairncross

Themes of ruthless and unrelenting tragedy are at the heart of these plays. The first two are based on Greek legend, while *Athaliah* depicts the vengeance and the power of the Old Testament Jehovah.

441220 320pp £6.99

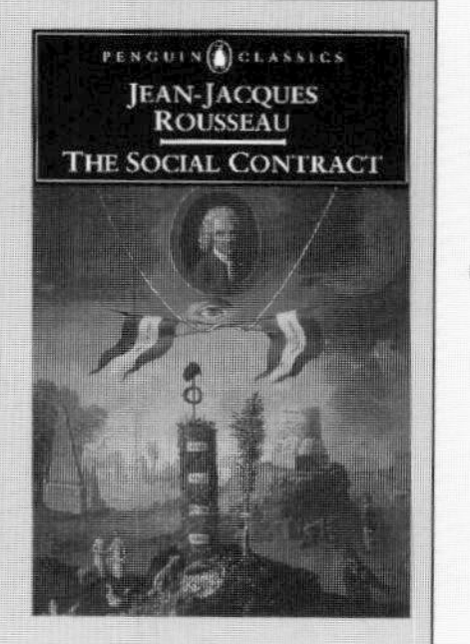

ARTHUR RIMBAUD

1854–1891

COLLECTED POEMS

Translated with an introduction by
Oliver Bernard

All the symbolist poet's well-known poems are included in this volume along with a selection of Rimbaud's letters. Both letters and poems are presented in English prose translations as well as the original French.

420649 384pp £8.99

JEAN-JACQUES ROUSSEAU

1712–1778

THE CONFESSIONS

Translated with an introduction by
J M Cohen

The posthumously published *Confessions*, which describes the first fifty-three years of the author's life with a refreshing frankness, has left an indelible imprint on the thought of successive generations, influencing, among others, Proust, Goethe and Tolstoy.

44033X 608pp £8.99

A DISCOURSE ON INEQUALITY

Translated and annotated with an introduction by Maurice Cranston

The most influential of Rousseau's writings, the 'Second Discourse' set forth a theory of human evolution that prefigured the discoveries of Darwin, revolutionized the study of anthropology and linguistics, and made a seminal contribution to political and social thought – leading to both the French Revolution and the birth of social science.

444394 192pp £5.99

EMILE

Translated with an introduction by
Allan Bloom

In *Emile* Rousseau describes an imaginary attempt to transform a young boy into an autonomous, morally and intellectually independent – that is to say, truly democratic – human being. In the process he presents an egalitarian politics that attempts to reconcile nature with history, human selfishness with the demands of civil society and, hence, inclination with duty.

445633 512pp £8.99

REVERIES OF THE SOLITARY WALKER

Translated with an introduction and brief chronology by Peter France

Ten meditations written in the two years before Rousseau's death in 1778 provide an excellent introduction to the thinker's complex world, expressing in its full force the agony of isolation and alienation.

443630 160pp £6.99

THE SOCIAL CONTRACT

Translated with an introduction by
Maurice Cranston

The Social Contract describes the basic principles of democratic government, stressing that law is derived from the will of the people.

442014 192pp £5.99

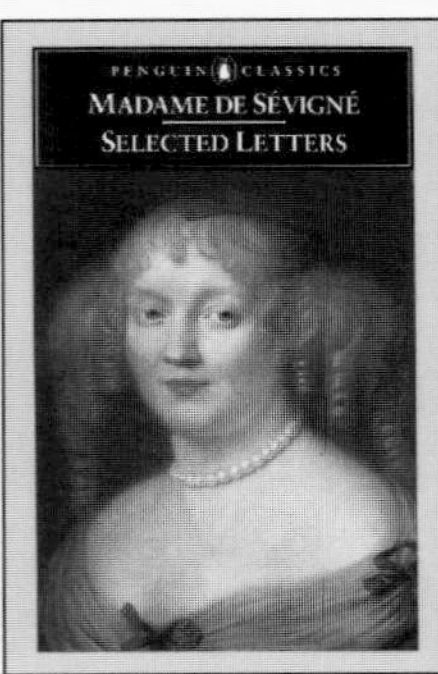

GEORGE SAND

1804–1876

Lettres d'un Voyageur

Translated by Sasha Rabinovitch and Patricia Thomson with an introduction by Patricia Thomson

In these remarkable letters, published as articles from 1834 to 1836, Sand's controversial approach to life is reflected in her provocative comments on art, music, religion, politics and the relations between the sexes.

444114 320pp £7.99

MADAME DE SEVIGNE

1626–1696

Selected Letters

Edited and translated with an introduction by Leonard Tancock

An extraordinary vivid picture of social, literary and political life in Louis XIV's France is captured in this selection of letters.

44405X 320pp £8.99

STENDHAL

1788–1842

The Charterhouse of Parma

Translated with an introduction by Margaret R B Shaw

This fictionalized account explores the intrigues within a small Italian court during the time of Napoleon's final exile.

440615 496pp £6.99

The Life of Henry Brulard

Translated with an introduction by John Sturrock

Frank, sardonic and wickedly amusing, Stendhal's autobiography reveals a man out of place in his times, not only in his comments on contemporary values, but most strikingly, in his assumption that childhood experiences shape a man – a belief more compatible to our post-Freudian age than to France in the 1830s.

446117 528pp £7.99

Love

Translated by Gilbert and Suzanne Sale with an introduction by Jean Stewart and B C J G Knight

Stendhal draws on history, literature and his own experiences in this intensely personal yet universal story of unrequited love.

44307X 336pp £7.99

Scarlet and Black

Translated with an introduction by Margaret R B Shaw

In the atmosphere of the fearful and greedy drawing-room conformity that followed Waterloo, Julian Sorel rebels against his circumstances and wills himself to make something of his life by adopting a code of hypocrisy and a life of crime.

440305 512pp £5.99

ALFRED DE VIGNY

1797–1863

THE SERVITUDE AND GRANDEUR OF ARMS

Translated with an introduction by Roger Gard

After legendary victories, Napoleon's armies collapsed. In this book, Alfred de Vigny – a royalist aristocrat and a poet of great distinction who also served as an unglamorous garrison officer – depicts a generation of soldiers bounded by peace yet still haunted by dreams of former glory.

44663X 208pp £7.99

VOLTAIRE

1694–1778

CANDIDE

Translated by John Butt

Voltaire takes Candide and Dr Pangloss through a variety of ludicrous adventures and reversals of fortune in this satirical challenge to the empty optimism prevalent in Voltaire's eighteenth-century society.

440046 144pp £2.50

LETTERS ON ENGLAND

Translated with an introduction by Leonard Tancock

Also known as the *Lettres anglaises ou philosophiques*, Voltaire's response to his exile in England offered the French public of 1734 a panoramic view of British culture. Perceiving them as a veiled attack against the ancien regime, however, the French government ordered the letters burned and Voltaire persecuted.

44386X 160pp £6.99

PHILOSOPHICAL DICTIONARY

Translated and edited with an introduction by Theodore Besterman

Voltaire's irony, scrutiny and passionate love of reason and justice are fully evident in this deliberately revolutionary series of essays on religion, metaphysics, society and government.

44257X 400pp £9.99

ZADIG/L'INGÉNU

Translated with an introduction by John Butt

One of Voltaire's earliest tales, *Zadig* is set in the exotic East and is told in the comic spirit of *Candide*; *L'Ingénu*, written after *Candide*, is a darker tale in which an American Indian records his impressions of France.

441263 192pp £6.99

ÉMILE ZOLA

1840–1902

L'ASSOMMOIR

Translated with an introduction by Leonard Tancock

A potent example of naturalist writing, which Zola fiercely advocated, this attempt is one of the first 'classical tragedies' to detail working-class existence in the slums of a great city.

442316 432pp £5.99

LA BÊTE HUMAINE

Translated with an introduction by Leonard Tancock

In this taut thriller of violent passions, crime and the law, Zola bitterly attacks the politics and corruption of the French judicial system.

443274 368p £5.99

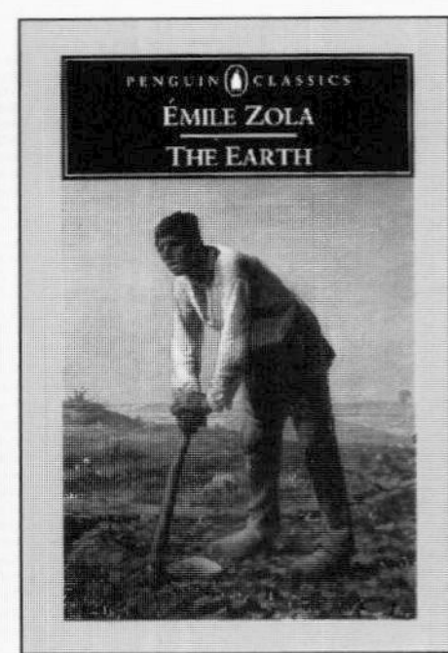

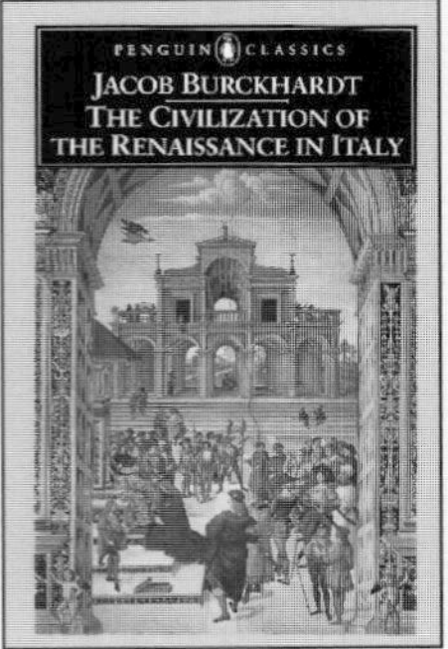

THE DÉBACLE

Translated by Leonard Tancock

Zola's only purely historical work, this realistic, detailed and accurate account of France's defeat in the Franco-Prussian War is a grim testament to the human horrors of war.

442804 512pp £6.99

THE EARTH

Translated with an introduction by Douglas Parmée

With humour and flashes of tenderness, Zola depicts the human cycle of birth, marriage and death against the natural changes of the agricultural seasons.

443878 512pp £6.99

GERMINAL

Translated with an introduction by Leonard Tancock

Written to draw attention to the misery prevailing among the lower classes France during the Second Empire, *Germinal* depicts the grim struggle between capital and labour in a coal field in northern France.

440453 512pp £5.99

NANA

Translated with an introduction by George Holden

An evocation of the corrupt world of the Second Empire, this story of a prostitute embodies Zola's theory that behaviour is predetermined by one's origin.

442634 480pp £5.99

THÉRÈSE RAQUIN

Translated with an introduction by Leonard Tancock

This tale of adultery, murder and revenge, condemned as pornography when it was published in 1867, is one of Zola's earliest novels.

441204 256pp £5.99

GERMAN LITERATURE

GEORG BÜCHNER

1813–1837

COMPLETE PLAYS AND LENZ AND OTHER WRITINGS

Translated with an introduction by John Reddick

Collected in this volume are powerful dramas and psychological fiction by the nineteenth-century iconoclast now recognized as a major figure of world literature. Also included are selections from Büchner's letters and philosophical writings.

445862 366pp £7.99

JACOB BURCKHARDT

1818–1897

THE CIVILIZATION OF THE RENAISSANCE IN ITALY

Translated by S G C Middlemore with a new introduction by Peter Burke

In this influential interpretation of the Italian Renaissance, Burckhardt explores the political and psychological forces that marked the beginning of the modern world.

44534X 400pp £9.99

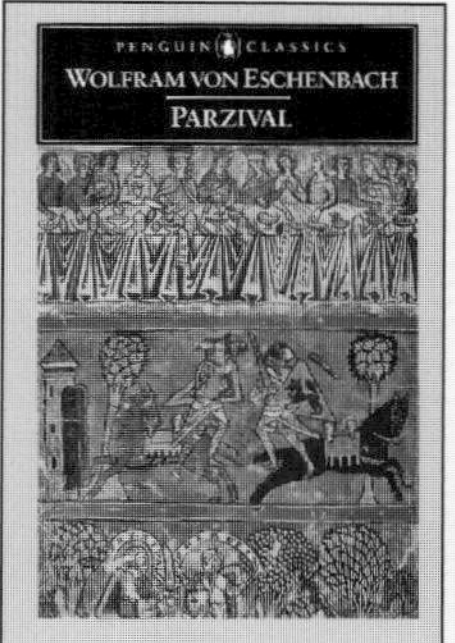

CARL VON CLAUSEWITZ
1780–1831

ON WAR
Edited with an introduction by Anatol Rapoport and translated by J J Graham

This treatise presents the great Prussian soldier's views both on total war and on war as a continuation of foreign policy.

444270 464pp £8.99

MEISTER ECKHART
c. 1260–1327

SELECTED WRITINGS
Edited and translated with an introduction by Oliver Davies

Selected Writings illuminates the German Dominican Meister Eckhart's synthesis of traditional Christian belief and Greek metaphysics, yielding a boldly speculative philosophy founded on 'oneness' of the universe and on a God at once personal and transcendent.

433430 336pp £8.99

FRIEDRICH ENGELS
1820–1895

THE CONDITION OF THE WORKING CLASS IN ENGLAND
Edited with a foreword by Victor Kiernan

Introducing ideas further developed in *The Communist Manifesto*, this savage indictment of the bourgeoisie studies British factory, mine and farm workers – graphically portraying the human suffering born of the Industrial Revolution.

444866 304pp £7.99

THE ORIGIN OF THE FAMILY
Introduction by Michele Barrett

In a cornerstone of Communist theory that is also a fundamental feminist work, Engels examines private property and its relationship to the subjugation of women.

444653 240pp £6.99

WOLFRAM VON ESCHENBACH
c. 1170–1220

PARZIVAL
Translated by Arthur Hatto

A prose translation of Wolfram von Eschenbach's thirteenth-century narrative poem re-creates and completes the story of the Holy Grail, left unfinished by Chrétien de Troyes.

443614 448pp £9.99

THEODOR FONTANE
1819–1898

EFFI BRIEST
Translated with an introduction by Douglas Parmée

This story of a woman's adultery and its consequences is a stunning portrait of the rigidity of the Prussian aristocracy in the mid-nineteenth century.

441905 272pp £6.99

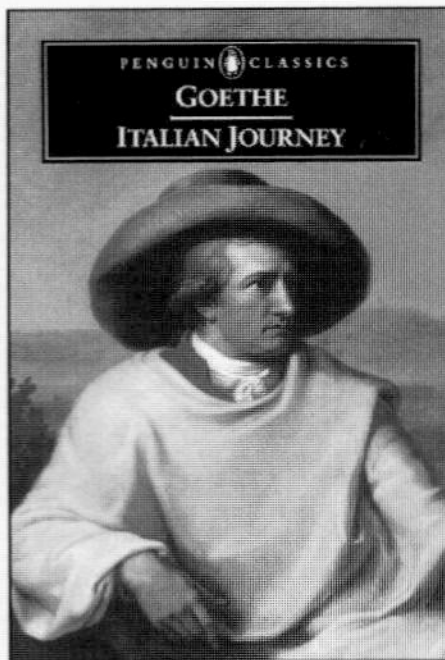

Two Novellas

The Woman Taken in Adultery and *The Poggenpuhl Family*

Translated with notes by Gabrielle Annan, with an introduction by Erich Heller

The Woman Taken in Adultery is a tale of adultery in 1880s Berlin with a happy ending. *The Poggenpuhl Family* poignantly evokes the lives of an aristocratic Berlin family struggling in genteel poverty.

435247 272pp £6.99

GERMAN IDEALIST PHILOSOPHY

Edited with an introduction by Rüdiger Bubner

The era of German Idealism is among the most inspiring and spirited in Western philosophical history. Rüdiger Bubner's anthology of key texts and lesser known extracts, along with helpful overviews of each philosopher, makes the perfect introduction to Idealist philosophy.

446605 368pp £9.99

JOHANN WOLFGANG VON GOETHE

1749–1832

Elective Affinities

Translated with an introduction by R J Hollingdale

Condemned as immoral when it was first published, this novel reflects the conflict Goethe felt between his respect for the conventions of marriage and the possibility of spontaneous passion.

442421 304pp £7.99

Faust, Part One

Translated with an introduction by Philip Wayne

Goethe's masterpiece dramatizes the struggle of modern man to solve the mysteries of energy, pleasure and the creation of life.

440127 208pp £5.99

Faust, Part Two

Translated with an introduction by Philip Wayne

Rich in allusion and allegory, *Faust, Part Two* explores philosophical themes that obsessed Goethe throughout his life.

440933 288pp £5.99

Italian Journey 1786–1788

Translated with an introduction by W H Auden and Elizabeth Mayer

Goethe's account of his passage through Italy is a great travel chronicle as well as a candid self-portrait of a genius in the grip of spiritual crisis.

442332 512pp £8.99

Maxims and Reflections

Translated by Elizabeth Stopp

Edited with an introduction by Peter Hutchinson

Throughout his long, hectic and astonishingly varied life, Goethe would jot down his passing thoughts on theatre programmes, visiting cards, draft manuscripts and even bills. His 1,413 maxims and reflections reveal some of his deepest thoughts on art, ethics, literature and natural science, as well as his immediate

reactions to books, chance encounters or administrative work.

447202 208pp £7.99

NEW AUGUST 98

SELECTED VERSE

Translated with an introduction by
David Luke

This dual-language edition of nearly three hundred poems draws from every period of Goethe's work, and includes substantial portions of *Faust*.

420746 416pp £8.99

THE SORROWS OF YOUNG WERTHER

Translated with an introduction by
Michael Hulse

Based partly on Goethe's unrequited love for Charlotte Buff, this novel of pathological sensibility strikes a powerful blow against Enlightenment rationalism.

44503X 144pp £6.99

GOTTFRIED VON STRASSBURG

c. 12–13th century

TRISTAN

Translated with an introduction by
Arthur Hatto

This medieval version of the legendary romance between Tristan and Isolde portrays Tristan as a sophisticated pre-Renaissance man.

440984 384pp £8.99

JACOB AND WILHELM GRIMM

1785–1863 & 1786–1859

SELECTED TALES

Translated with an introduction by
David Luke

Sixty-five newly translated selections from *Kinder – und Hausmärchen* provide a representative sample of the folktale motifs that have fascinated children and adults around the world for centuries.

444017 432pp £7.99

HEGEL

1770–1831

INTRODUCTORY LECTURES ON AESTHETICS

Translated by Bernard Bosanquet with
an introduction and commentary by
Michael Inwood

Hegel's writings on art – and his profound conclusion that art was in terminal decline – have had a broad impact on our culture.

43335X 240pp £7.99

HEINRICH HEINE

1797–1856

SELECTED PROSE

Edited and translated with an introduction
by Ritchie Robertson

This collection of extraordinary prose – meditations on spiritualism and sensualism, evocative travel narratives, memoirs of his Jewish childhood, and much more – exemplifies the artistry of the great German poet.

445552 368pp £9.99

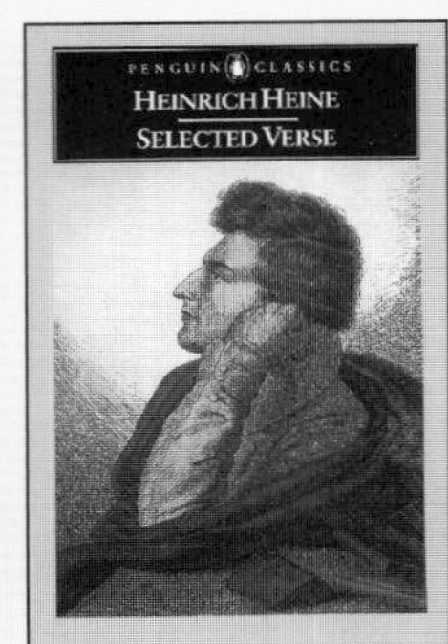

SELECTED VERSE

Edited and translated with an introduction by Peter Branscombe

This anthology includes a selection of poems in their original German, along with English prose translations, from Heine: a restless and homeless Jew among Germans, a German in Paris, a rebel among the bourgeoisie and always, a man divided against himself.

420983 304pp £8.99

ERNST THEODOR HOFFMANN

1776–1822

THE LIFE AND OPINIONS OF THE TOMCAT MURR

Translated by Anthea Bell with an introduction by Jeremy Adler

In this astonishing book, a vain and very bourgeois tomcat sets out to write his memoirs, using a biography of Kreisler as a blotting pad. By a printer's error, the two lives get spliced together into a bizarre double narrative.

446311 384pp £7.99

NEW APRIL 99

TALES OF HOFFMANN

Selected and translated with an introduction by R J Hollingdale

Eight of Hoffmann's best and best-known tales are retold in this collection – among them 'Mademoiselle de Scudery', 'Doge and Dogeressa' and 'The Sandman', which forms the basis for the first half of Offenbach's opera.

443924 416pp £8.99

FRIEDRICH HÖLDERLIN

1770–1843

SELECTED POEMS AND FRAGMENTS

Selected by Jeremy Adler, translated with a new preface and introduction by Michael Hamburger

Friedrich Hölderlin is now recognized as one of Europe's supreme poets. This superb bilingual selection is the definitive English version of a giant of German literature.

424164 400pp £8.99

ALEXANDER VON HUMBOLDT

1769–1859

PERSONAL NARRATIVE OF A JOURNEY TO THE EQUINOCTIAL REGIONS OF THE NEW CONTINENT

Abridged and translated with an introduction by Jason Wilson

Historical introduction by Malcolm Nicolson

With *Personal Narrative*, the German scientist and explorer Alexander von Humboldt invented the art of travel writing. Translated into English for the first time since 1851, this edition demonstrates Humboldt's extraordinary ability to present scientific observations and information in an entertaining, engaging style.

445536 400pp £7.99

HEINRICH VON KLEIST

1777–1811

THE MARQUISE OF O – AND OTHER STORIES

Translated with an introduction by David Luke and Nigel Reeves

Between 1799, when he left the Prussian

Army, and his suicide in 1811, Kleist developed into a writer of unprecedented and tragically isolated genius. This collection of works from the last period of his life also includes 'The Earthquake in Chile', 'Michael Kohlhaas', 'The Beggarwoman of Locarno', 'St Cecilia or The Power of Music', 'The Betrothal in Santo Domingo', 'The Foundling' and 'The Duel'.
443592 320pp £7.99

GEORG CHRISTOPH LICHTENBERG

1742–1799

Aphorisms

Translated with an introduction by
R J Hollingdale

This collection of pithy and witty sayings by the man who first introduced the aphorism to Germany, mocks some of the principal men and movements of the Enlightenment.
445196 208pp £6.99

KARL MARX

1818–1883

Capital Volume 1

Translated by Ben Fowkes and with
an introduction by Ernest Mandel

This 1867 study - one of the most influential documents of modern times - looks at the relationship between labour and value, the role of money, and the conflict between the classes.
445684 1152pp £15.99

Capital Volume 2

Translated by David Fernbach and with an
introduction by Ernest Mandel

The 'forgotten' second volume of *Capital*, Marx's world-shaking analysis of economics, politics and history, contains the vital discussion of commodity, the cornerstone to Marx's theories.
445692 624pp £12.00

Capital Volume 3

Translated by David Fernbach and with an
introduction by Ernest Mandel

The third volume of the book that changed the course of world history, *Capital*'s final chapters were Marx's most controversial writings on the subject and were never completed.
445706 1088pp £15.00

Early Writings

Translated by Rodney Livingstone and
Gregor Benton with an introduction by
Lucio Colletti

In this rich body of early work the foundations of Marxism can be seen in essays on alienation, the state, democracy, and human nature.
445749 464pp £10.99

Grundrisse

Translated with a foreword by
Martin Nicolaus

Written between *The Communist Manifesto* (1848) and the first volume of *Capital* (1867), *Grundrisse* provides the only outline of his full political-economic theories.
445757 912pp £16.00

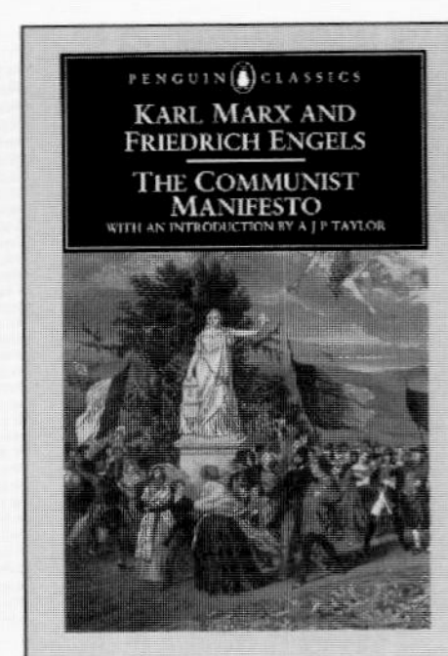

POLITICAL WRITINGS VOLUME 1 REVOLUTIONS OF 1848

Edited with an introduction by David Fernbach

The first of a three-volume collection, the *Revolutions* is a study of the failed European revolutions, and Marx's call for an independent workers' organization to begin the 'permanent revolution'. Includes the *Manifesto of the Communist Party.*

445714 368pp £8.99

POLITICAL WRITINGS VOLUME 3 FIRST INTERNATIONAL AND AFTER

Edited with an introduction by David Fernbach

In this third volume of *Political Writings*, Marx applies the pioneering insights of *Capital* to ongoing international events and foresees the possibility of revolution in Russia.

445730 432pp £11.00

KARL MARX AND FRIEDRICH ENGELS

1818-1883 1820–1895

THE COMMUNIST MANIFESTO

Translated by Samuel Moore and with an introduction by A J P Taylor

This compelling document is even more relevant today in light of the downfall of Communism. It includes a special introduction by the noted British historian A J P Taylor.

444785 128pp £2.50

KARL PHILIPP MORITZ

1756–1793

ANTON REISER

Translated with an introduction by Ritchie Robertson

In this memorable autobiographical novel Moritz turned his emotionally turbulent early life into the unsparing story of a shy, lonely youth struggling to find his place in the rigidly stratified social order of late-eighteenth-century Germany.

446095 400pp £8.99

FRIEDRICH NIETZSCHE

1844–1900

BEYOND GOOD AND EVIL

Translated by R J Hollingdale and with an introduction by Michael Tanner

Nietzsche discusses how cultures lose their creative drives and become decadent, offering a wealth of fresh insights into such themes as the self-destructive urge of Christianity, the prevalence of 'slave moralities' and the dangers of the pursuit of philosophical or scientific truth.

445137 240pp £6.99

THE BIRTH OF TRAGEDY

Edited with an introduction by Michael Tanner

Translated by Shaun Whiteside

Nietzsche's first book, published in 1871 and now a seminal work of Western culture, is filled with passionate energy and argument probing the relationship between our experiences of suffering in life and in art, myths and legends.

433392 160pp £6.99

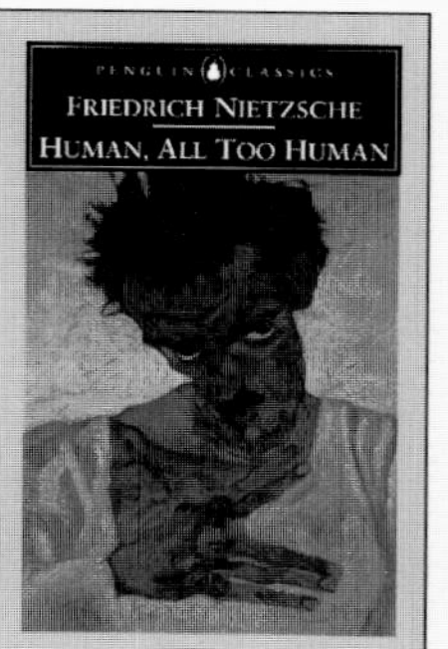

Ecce Homo

Translated by R J Hollingdale with an introduction by Michael Tanner

This strange and moving autobiography of Nietzsche was begun in late 1888, weeks before his final psychological breakdown.

445153 144pp £6.99

Human, All Too Human

Translated by Marion Faber and Stephen Lehmann with an introduction by Marion Faber

This book sketches in Nietzsche's key theories about the will to power, the need to transcend Christian morality and the élite Free Spirits who live untrammelled by convention. Rejecting the style and spirit of German romanticism and returning to sources in the French Enlightenment, Nietzsche sets out his unsettling views on topics ranging from art, arrogance and boredom to passion, science, vanity, women and youth.

446176 304pp £6.99

A Nietzsche Reader

Selected and translated with an introduction by R J Hollingdale

Designed to give an overview of Nietzsche's thought, of his approach to the conventional problems of Western philosophy, and of his own philosophy of 'the will to power', this anthology includes 240 thematically arranged passages from his major philosophical works.

443290 288pp £7.99

Thus Spoke Zarathustra

Translated and introduced by R J Hollingdale

Nietzsche's most accessible work, this spiritual odyssey through the modern world influenced such writers as Shaw, Lawrence, Mann and Sartre.

441182 352pp £7.99

Twilight of the Idols The Anti-Christ

Translated by R J Hollingdale and with an introduction by Michael Tanner

Written in 1888, before he succumbed to insanity, *Twilight of the Idols* is a fascinating summation of Nietzsche's rejection of the prevalent ideas of his time; *The Anti-Christ* is his passionate challenge to institutional Christianity.

445145 208pp £6.99

FRIEDRICH SCHILLER

1759–1805

The Robbers Wallenstein

Translated with an introduction by F J Lamport

The foremost dramatist of German classicism wrote *The Robbers*, his first play, in 1781; in the trilogy *Wallenstein*, written nineteen years later, Schiller tried to combine the strengths of Sophocles, Shakespeare and French classical drama.

443681 480pp £8.99

Mary Stuart

Translated with an introduction by
F J Lamport

Ranking almost with Goethe as a central figure in the golden age of German literature, Friedrich Schiller built this superb drama around the conflict between Elizabeth I and Mary, Queen of Scots.

447113 176pp £6.99

ARTHUR SCHOPENHAUER

1788–1860

Essays and Aphorisms

Translated with an introduction by
R J Hollingdale

This selection of thoughts on religion, ethics, politics, women, suicide, books and much more is taken from Schopenhauer's last work, *Parerga and Paralipomena*, published in 1851.

442278 240pp £6.99

ITALIAN LITERATURE

LEON BATTISTA ALBERTI

1404–1472

On Painting

Translated by Cecil Grayson with an
introduction by Martin Kemp

The first book devoted to the intellectual rationale for painting, Alberti's discussion of the process of vision, painting techniques, and the moral and artistic prerequisites of the artist remains a classic of art theory.

433317 112pp £6.99

THOMAS AQUINAS

c. 1225–1274

Selected Writings

Edited and translated with
an introduction by Ralph McInerny

Although a controversial figure in his own day, Thomas Aquinas forged a unique synthesis of faith and reason, of ancient philosophy and sacred scripture, which decisively influenced Dante and the whole subsequent Catholic tradition. In this superb selection, arranged chronologically, Ralph McInerny brings together sermons, commentaries, responses to criticism and substantial extracts from one of Christianity's supreme masterpieces, the Summa theologiae.

436324 880pp £12.99
NEW JUNE 98

LUDOVICO ARIOSTO

1474–1535

Orlando Furioso

Translated with an introduction by
Barbara Reynolds

A dazzling kaleidoscope of adventures, ogres, monsters, barbaric splendour and romance, this epic poem stands as one of the greatest works of the Italian Renaissance.

Volume 1

443118 832pp £12.00

Volume 2

44310X 800pp £15.00

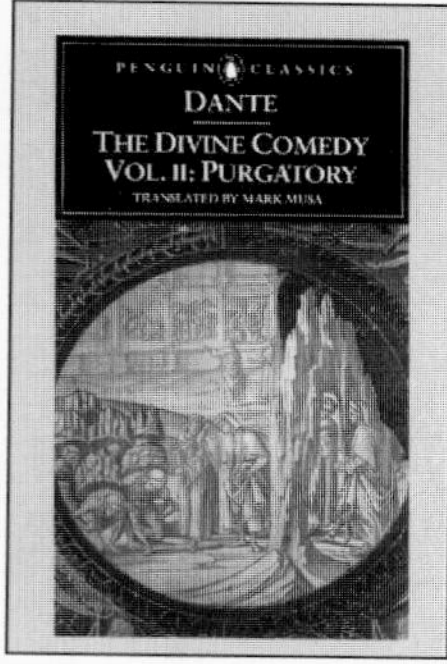

GIOVANNI BOCCACCIO

1313–1375

THE DECAMERON

Translated with an introduction by G H McWilliam

Read as a social document of medieval times, as an earthly counterpart of Dante's *Divine Comedy*, or even as an early manifestation of the dawning spirit of the Renaissance, *The Decameron* is a masterpiece of imaginative narrative whose background is the Florentine plague of 1348.

44629X 1072pp £7.99

CASTIGLIONE

1478–1529

THE BOOK OF THE COURTIER

Translated with an introduction by George Bull

Discretion, decorum, nonchalance, and gracefulness are qualities of the complete and perfect Italian Renaissance courtier that are outlined in this series of imaginary conversations between the principal members of the court of Urbino in 1507.

441921 368pp £7.99

BENVENUTO CELLINI

1500–1571

AUTOBIOGRAPHY

Translated by George Bull

Revised and expanded edition with a new chronology and notes

Benvenuto Cellini was a celebrated goldsmith and distinguished sculptor, yet it is on his autobiography that much of his fame rests. Begun in Florence when he was fifty-eight, it was primarily intended to be the story of his life and art, his tragedies and triumphs. However, as he was an active participant in the wars and struggles of the period and drew his friends and enemies from all levels of society, it became a vivid and convincing portrait of the manners and morals both of the rulers of the sixteenth century and their subjects.

447180 512pp £9.99

NEW MARCH 99

DANTE

1265–1321

THE DIVINE COMEDY VOLUME 1: INFERNO

Translated with an introduction and commentary by Mark Musa

This vigorous new blank-verse translation of the poet's journey through the circles of Hell re-creates for the modern reader the rich meanings that Dante's poem had for his contemporaries while preserving his simple, natural style and capturing the swift movement of the original Italian verse.

444416 432pp £6.99

VOLUME 2: PURGATORY

Translated with an introduction and commentary by Mark Musa

444424 428pp £6.99

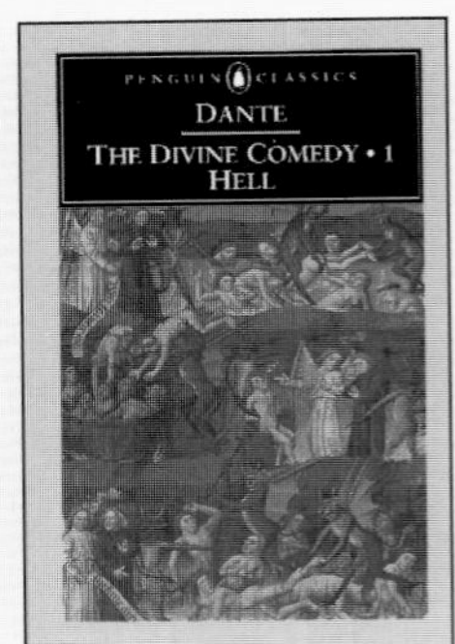

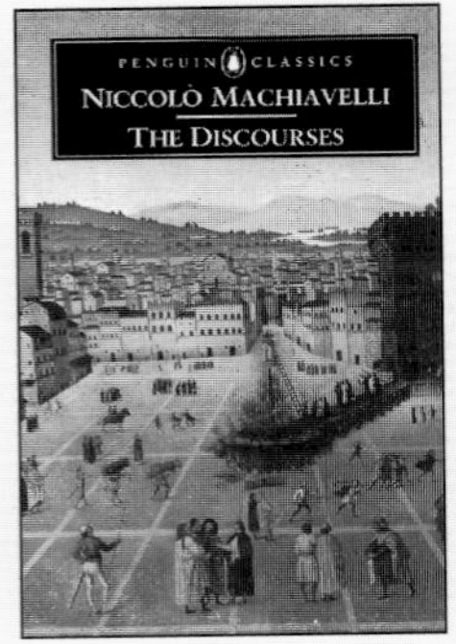

VOLUME 3: PARADISE

Translated with an introduction and commentary by Mark Musa

Dante relates his mystical interpretation of the heavens, and his moment of transcendent glory, as he journeys, first with Beatrice, then alone, toward the Trinity.

444432 464pp £6.99

THE DIVINE COMEDY VOLUME 1: HELL

Translated with an introduction by Dorothy L Sayers

This is a revered translation that attempts to reveal Dante through his classic work as a poet of vivid personality: sublime, intellectual, humorous, simple and tender.

440062 352pp £6.99

VOLUME 2: PURGATORY

Translated with an introduction by Dorothy L Sayers

In *Purgatory*, Dante deals with the origins of sin as he struggles up the terraces of Mount Purgatory on his arduous journey toward God.

440461 400pp £6.99

VOLUME 3: PARADISE

Translated by Dorothy L Sayers and Barbara Reynolds with an introduction by Barbara Reynolds

441050 400pp £6.99

LA VITA NUOVA

Translated with an introduction by Barbara Reynolds

This series of astonishing and tender love poems to Beatrice is interspersed with Dante's own explanations of their sources and detailed analyses of their structure.

442162 128pp £5.99

MACHIAVELLI

1469–1527

THE DISCOURSES

Translated by Leslie J Walker with revisions by Brian Richardson, edited with an introduction by Bernard Crick

Machiavelli examines the glorious republican past of Rome. In contrast with *The Prince*, this unfinished work upholds the Republic as the best and most enduring style of government.

444289 544pp £8.99

THE PRINCE

Translated by George Bull with an introduction by Anthony Grafton

This famous treatise on statecraft expounds Machiavelli's principles for building a government that will last – stating uncompromisingly what most governments do but none profess to do.

447520 144pp £2.99

ALESSANDRO MANZONI

1785–1873

The Betrothed

Translated with an introduction by
Bruce Penman

Manzoni chronicle the perils of two lovers caught in the turbulence of seventeenth-century Italy.

44274X 720pp £8.99

MARCO POLO

1254–1324

The Travels

Translated with an introduction by
Ronald Latham

Despite piracy, shipwreck, brigandage and wild beasts, Polo moved in a world of highly organized commerce. This chronicle of his travel through Asia, whether read as fact or fiction, is alive with adventures, geographical information, and descriptions of natural phenomena.

440577 384pp £7.99

GIORGIO VASARI

1511–1574

Lives of the Artists Volume 1

Translated and edited with an introduction by George Bull

Vasari offers insights into the lives and techniques of twenty artists, from Cimabue, Giotto, and Leonardo to Michelangelo and Titian.

445005 480pp £7.99

Volume 2

Translated and edited with an introduction by George Bull and notes on the artists by Peter Murray

Vasari's knowledge was based on his own experience as an early Renaissance painter and architect. Volume 2 explores the lives of twenty-five artists, from Perugino to Giovanni Pisano.

444602 400pp £7.99

POLISH LITERATURE

JAN POTOCKI

1761–1815

The Manuscript Found in Saragossa

Translated with an introduction by
Ian Maclean

Written in French by Polish-born Jan Potocki, probably between 1797 and 1815, this nest of stories drives the reader ever deeper into a labyrinth of sadism, satanism, the cabbala and other phantoms brought forth by the sleep of eighteenth-century Reason. As well as being one of the great masterpieces of subversion, it is also an encyclopaedia of the dark side of the European Enlightenment.

445803 656pp £8.99

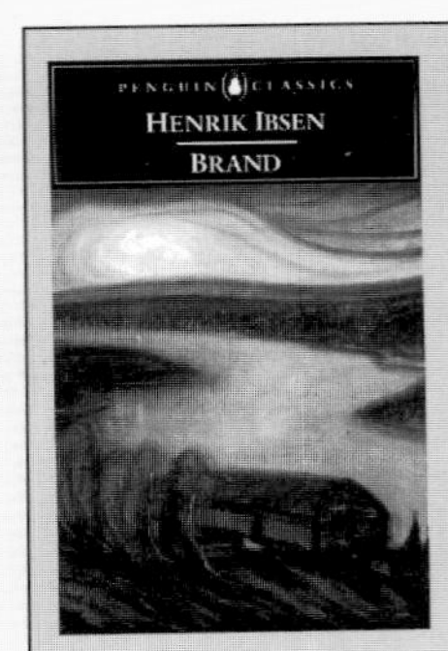

SCANDINAVIAN LITERATURE

HENRIK IBSEN

1828–1906

BRAND

Translated by Geoffrey Hill

The story of a minister driven by faith to risk the death of his wife and child, *Brand* pits a man of vision against the forces of ignorance and venality.

446761 176pp £6.99

A DOLL'S HOUSE
THE LEAGUE OF YOUTH
THE LADY FROM THE SEA

Translated with an introduction by Peter Watts

From *The League of Youth*, his first venture into realistic social drama, to *A Doll's House*, a provocative portrait of a woman's struggle for freedom, to the family tensions depicted in *The Lady from the Sea*, Ibsen is concerned with the individual's conflicts with society.

441468 336pp £6.99

GHOSTS
A PUBLIC ENEMY
WHEN WE DEAD WAKE

Translated with an introduction by Peter Watts

Incisive, critical and controversial, *Ghosts* and *A Public Enemy* depict the negative effects of social rigidity on individual lives; *When We Dead Awaken*, Ibsen's last play, is a story of internal turmoil that can be read as the dramatist's comments on his lifework.

441352 304pp £5.99

HEDDA GABLER
THE PILLARS OF THE COMMUNITY
THE WILD DUCK

Translated with an introduction by Una Ellis-Fermor

The Pillars of the Community and *The Wild Duck* show Ibsen's preoccupation with problems of personal and social morality; *Hedda Gabler*, the latest of these plays, is both a drama of individual conflict and a partial return to social themes.

44016X 368pp £6.99

THE MASTER BUILDER AND OTHER PLAYS

The Master Builder

Rosmersholm

Little Eylof

John Gabriel Borkman

Translated with an introduction by Una Ellis-Fermor

The four plays collected here were written late in Ibsen's career and reflect his then growing interests in internal conflicts and the dangers of self-deception.

440534 384pp £6.99

PEER GYNT

Translated with an introduction by Peter Watts

This high-spirited poetical fantasy, based on Norwegian folklore, is the story of an irresponsible, loveable hero. After its publication, Ibsen abandoned the verse form for more realistic prose plays.

441670 224pp £5.99

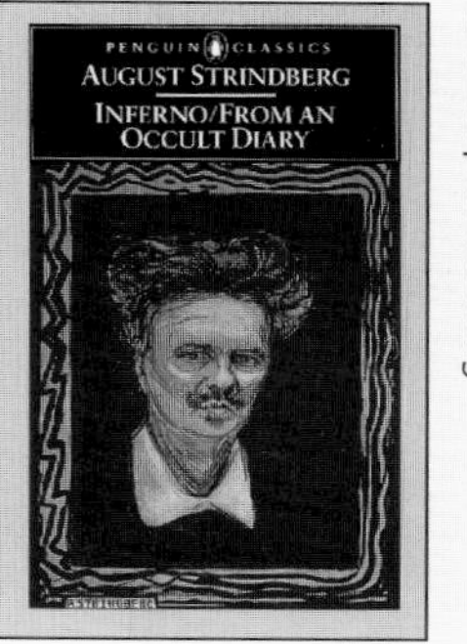

SØREN KIERKEGAARD
1813–1855

EITHER/OR
Abridged and translated with an introduction by Alastair Hannay

The first major work by the precursor of existentialism examines the philosophical choice between aesthetic and romantic life versus ethical and domestic life, and offers profound observations on the meaning of choice itself. Sheltering behind the persona of a fictitious editor, Kierkegaard brings together a diverse range of material, including reflections on Mozart and the famous 'Seducer's Diary'.

445773 640pp £9.99

FEAR AND TREMBLING
Translated with an introduction by Alastair Hannay

Abraham's unreserved submission to God's will provides the focus for this religious and ethical polemic. Originally written under the pseudonym of Johannes de Silentio, this is a key work in the psychology of religious belief.

444491 160pp £6.99

PAPERS AND JOURNALS: A SELECTION
Translated with an introduction by Alastair Hannay

This selection provides a comprehensive survey of the magnificent variety of Kierkegaard's work. In his papers and journals, we are privy to some of the philosopher's most private thoughts, and the effects of his beliefs upon his life.

445897 704pp £8.99

SICKNESS UNTO DEATH
Translated with an introduction by Alastair Hannay

Arguing that true Christianity exists only in accordance with free will, Kierkegaard's stern treatise attacks Hegelianism and the established Church, and breaks ground for existentialism and modern theology.

445331 192pp £6.99

AUGUST STRINDBERG
1849–1912

BY THE OPEN SEA
Translated with an introduction by Mary Sandbach

Axel Borg, a hypersensitive intellectual, has taken a post as an Inspector of Fisheries. His mission is to help the inhabitants of the outermost islands in the Stockholm archipelago to safeguard their declining fishing industry. But Borg's attempts are met with hostility and suspicion, and his contempt for these 'small people' and their primitive society grows. Finally alienated from nature as well as his fellow beings, Borg chooses total solitude as the path to freedom ... yet, ironically, it serves only to hasten his tragic end.

444882 208pp £6.99

INFERNO AND FROM AN OCCULT DIARY
Translated with an introduction by Mary Sandbach and selected by Torsten Eklund

Inferno is an intensely powerful record of Strindberg's mental collapse; *From an Occult Diary* recounts his obsessive, unrequited love for his third wife.

443649 432pp £8.99

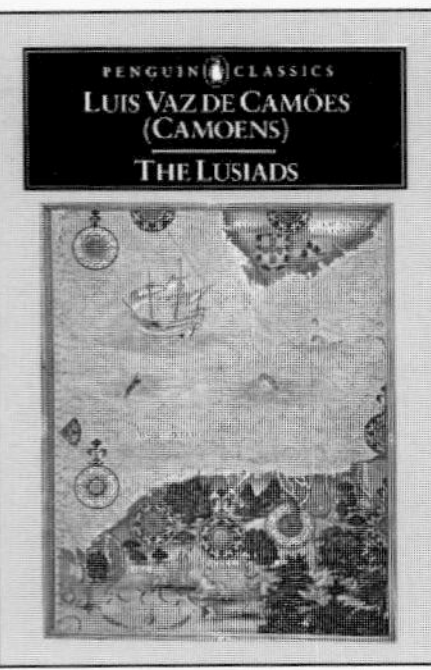

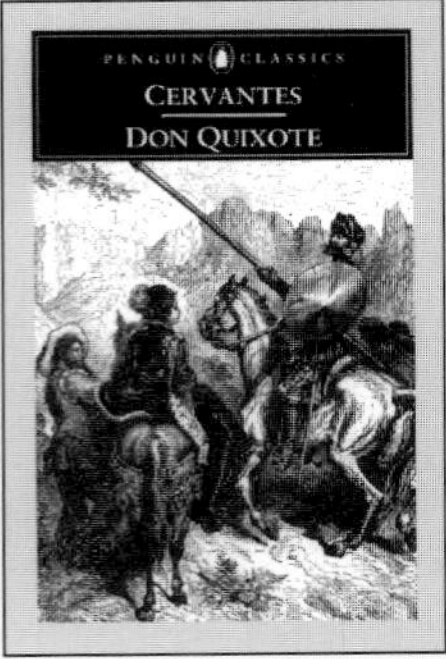

Three Plays

The Father

Miss Julia

Easter

Translated with an introduction by
Peter Watts

Combining acute psychological insight and masterful language, Strindberg depicts the war between the sexes in *The Father* and class struggle in *Miss Julie*; *Easter* is a mystical play, written after Strindberg underwent a religious conversion.

440828 176pp £5.99

SPANISH & PORTUGUESE LITERATURE

LEOPOLDO ALAS

1852–1901

La Regenta

Translated with an introduction by
John Rutherford

An outstanding work of nineteenth-century Spanish literature, this novel set in a provincial town explores an intelligent woman's unsuccessful quest for fulfilment through marriage, adultery and religion.

443460 736pp £9.99

BARTOLOMÉ DE LAS CASAS

1474–1566

A Short Account of the Destruction of the Indies

Translated by Nigel Griffin with an introduction by Anthony Pagden

No work is a stronger, more exacting, heartbreaking record of the Spanish atrocities in the genocidal enterprise of colonization in the Americas. This account provides an eyewitness's history of the process in the territory of Columbus.

445625 192pp £7.99

LUÍS VAS DE CAMÕES

1525–1580

The Lusiads

Translated with an introduction by
William Atkinson

Employing *The Aeneid* as a model and invoking the whole divine order of Olympus, *The Lusiads* – the national epic of Portugal – recounts the ten-month voyage by which Vasco da Gama opened the seaway to India.

440267 256pp £7.99

MIGUEL DE CERVANTES SAAVEDRA

1547–1615

The Adventures of Don Quixote

Translated with an introduction by
J M Cohen

The adventures of Cervantes' idealistic knight-errant and his simple but astute squire, Sancho Panza, is not only a hilarious parody of the romances of chivalry but an exploration of the relationship between the real and the illusionary.

440100 944pp £6.99

Exemplary Stories

Translated with an introduction by C A Jones

Included in this collection are 'The Little Gypsy Girl', 'Rinconete and Cortadillo', 'The Glass Graduate', 'Jealous Extremaduran', 'The Deceitful Marriage' and 'The Dog's Colloquy'.

442480 256pp £6.99

CHRISTOPHER COLUMBUS

c. 1451–1506

The Four Voyages

Edited and translated with an introduction by J M Cohen

This enthralling volume includes Columbus's letters and logbook and remains the definitive primary source on his voyages to Cuba, Haiti/Hispaniola, Jamaica, Trinidad and the Central American mainland.

442170 320pp £8.99

BERNAL DÍAZ DEL CASTILLO

1492–c. 1580

The Conquest of New Spain

Translated with an introduction by J M Cohen

Fifty years after the startling defeat of the Aztecs by Hernán Cortés and his small band of adventurers, Díaz writes a magnificent account on his experience as a soldier in Cortés's army.

441239 416pp £8.99

ST IGNATIUS OF LOYOLA

1491–1556

Personal Writings

Translated with introductions by Joseph A Munitiz and Philip Endean

The founder of the Jesuit order, Ignatius Loyola was one of the most influential figures of the Counter-Reformation. The works in this volume - *Reminiscences*, *The Spiritual Diary*, *The Spiritual Exercises* and selected letters - shed light on the more private aspects of Ignatius's life and beliefs.

433856 448pp £9.99

EMILIA PARDO BAZAN

1851–1921

The House of Ulloa

Translated with an introduction by Lucia Graves and Paul O'Prey

The House of Ulloa traces the decline of the old aristocracy at the time of the Glorious Revolution in 1868, while simultaneously exposing the moral vacuum at the heart of the new democracy. Its priest-hero, Father Julián, is a genuinely spiritual figure, tragically ineffectual in his struggle to prevent the fall of the House of Ulloa.

445021 288pp £6.99

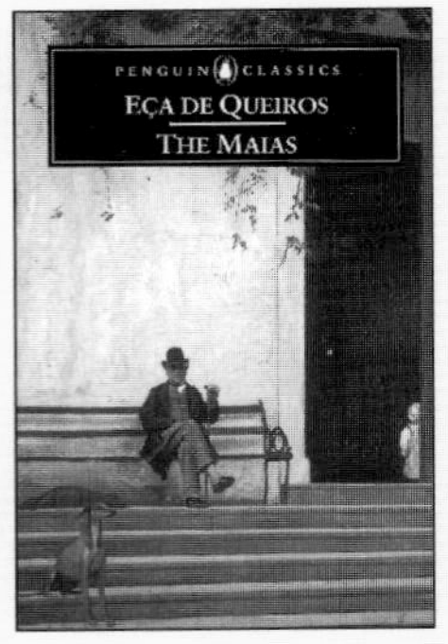

BENITO PEREZ GALDOS

1843–1920

FORTUNATA AND JACINTA TWO STORIES OF MARRIED WOMEN

Translated with an introduction by Agnes Moncy Gullón

Set against the political tumult of nineteenth-century Madrid, this controversial novel of love and obsession brings alive, in the tradition of Dickens and Balzac, the rich textures and traditions of its time.

433058 848pp £15.00

THE POEM OF THE CID

Translated by Rita Hamilton and Janet Perry with an introduction by Ian Michael

This epic poem, the only one to have survived from medieval Spain, depicts the career of the warlord El Cid in a unique blend of fiction and historical fact. Both English and Spanish texts are provided.

444467 256pp £7.99

ECA DE QUEIRÓS

1843–1900

THE MAIAS

Translated by Patricia McGowan Pinheiro and Ann Stevens, with an introduction by Nigel Griffin

Eca de Queirós was Portugal's greatest nineteenth-century novelist whose works brilliantly evoke – and condemn – the rapidly changing society of his times.

The Maias, generally considered his masterpiece, depicts the declining fortunes of a landowning family over three generations as they are gradually undermined by hypocrisy, complacency and sexual licence.

44694X 640pp £8.99

NEW NOVEMBER 98

TERESA OF ÁVILA

1515–1582

LIFE OF ST TERESA OF AVILA BY HERSELF

Translated with an introduction by J M Cohen

This story of how a wilful and unbalanced woman was transformed by profound religious experiences delves into the nature of exalted states. After *Don Quixote*, it is the most widely read prose classic of Spain.

440739 320pp £7.99

TWO SPANISH PICARESQUE NOVELS

Lazarillo de Tormes – Anon

The Swindler – Francisco de Quevedo

Translated by Michael Alpert

Lazarillo de Tormes (1554), the first and best of these essays in realism, describes the ingenious ruses employed by a boy from Salamanca to outwit his various masters. *The Swindler* (1626), by Francisco de Quevedo, represents the picaresque novel at its most sophisticated and witty in its account of the scatological adventure of a young servant who eventually sets up as a fake hidalgo in Madrid and earns his living by card-sharping.

442111 224pp £7.99

RUSSIAN LITERATURE

Courtesy of the David King Collection

ANTON CHEKHOV

1860–1904

The Duel and Other Stories

Translated with an introduction by
Ronald Wilks

Chekhov's mastery of the short story is illuminated in these examples: 'Murderer', 'My Wife', 'The Black Monk', 'Terror' and 'The Two Volodyas'.

444157 256pp £5.99

The Fiancée and Other Stories

Translated with an introduction by
Ronald Wilks

Although Chekhov is famed as a dramatist, he actually studied medicine in Moscow and launched his literary career through humorous contributions to journals. The stories in this selection demonstrate his prolific creativity: 'The Fiancée', 'On Official Business', 'Rothschild's Fiddle', 'Peasant Women', 'Three Years', 'With Friends', 'The Bet', 'New Villa', 'At a Country House', 'Beauties', 'His Wife' and 'The Student'.

44470X 240pp £5.99

The Kiss and Other Stories

Translated with an introduction by
Ronald Wilks

As Chekhov's confidence developed, his reputation grew along with his expertise. The stories in this collection represent his mature writings, including 'The Man in a Case', 'Gooseberries', 'Concerning Love', 'A Case History', 'In the Gully', 'Anna Round the Neck', 'The Kiss', 'Peasants', 'The Russian Master' and 'The Bishop'.

443363 224pp £4.99

Lady with Lapdog and Other Stories

Translated with an introduction by
David Magarshack

After the 1892 famine, Chekhov moved to a small estate not far from Moscow where he continued his pursuit of realistically characterising Russian society. 'Ward 6', one of the stories in this volume, was written there. Also included are 'Grief', 'Agafya', 'Misfortune', 'A Boring Story', 'The House with an Attic', 'Ionych' and 'The Daring'.

441433 288pp £5.99

The Party and Other Stories

Translated with an introduction by
Ronald Wilks

In addition to 'The Party', this volume includes 'A Woman's Kingdom', 'My Life: A Provincial's Story', 'An Unpleasant Business' and 'A Nervous Breakdown'.

444521 240pp £4.99

Plays

The Cherry Orchard/Three Sisters/
Ivanov/Uncle Vanya/The Bear/
The Proposal/ A Jubilee

Translated with an introduction by
Elisaveta Fen

Chekhov's realistic and sensitive plays revolve around a society on the brink of tremendous change.

440968 464pp £3.99

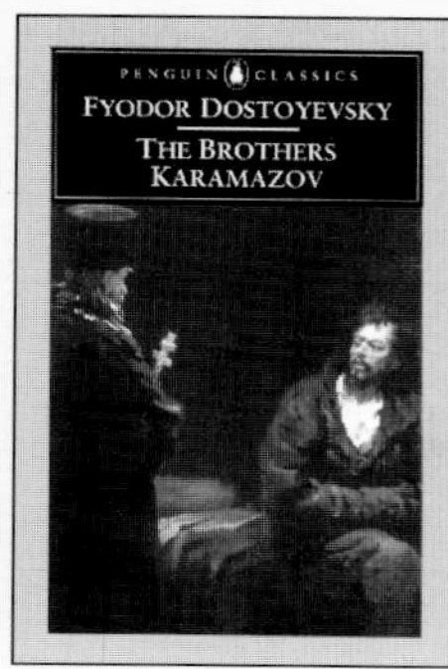

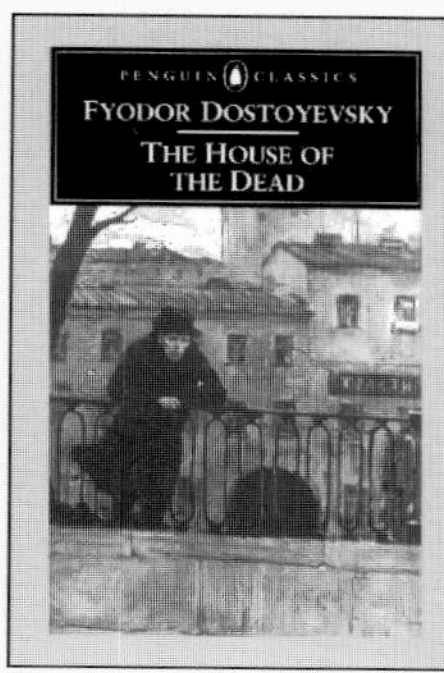

FYODOR DOSTOYEVSKY

1821–1881

The Brothers Karamazov

Translated with an introduction by
David McDuff

Dostoyevsky's masterful drama of parricide and family rivalry chronicles the murder of Fyodor Karamazov and the subsequent investigation and trial. This excellent translation recaptures the sound, tone and rough humour of the original.

445277 960pp £6.99

Crime and Punishment

Translated with an introduction by
David McDuff

Dostoyevsky's masterpiece of modern literature is a study in the psychology of the criminal mind, an indictment of social conditions and an engrossing portrait of Raskolnikov's Russia.

445285 656pp £2.99

The Devils

Translated with an introduction by
David Magarshack

Denounced by radical critics as the work of a reactionary, this powerful story of Russian terrorists who plot destruction only to murder one of their own seethes with provocative political opinions.

440356 704pp £6.99

The Gambler/Bobok/A Nasty Story

Translated with an introduction by
Jessie Coulson

Conveying all the intensity and futility of an obsession, 'The Gambler' is based on Dostoyevsky's firsthand experience; 'Bobok' and 'A Nasty Story' are two of the author's best darkly comic stories.

441794 240pp £5.99

The House of the Dead

Translated with an introduction by
David McDuff

The four years Dostoyevsky spent in a Siberian prison inform this portrait of convicts, their diverse stories, and prison life, rendered in almost documentary detail.

444564 368pp £5.99

The Idiot

Translated with an introduction by
David Magarshack

At the centre of a novel that has the plot of a thriller, Dostoyevsky portrays the Christlike figure of Prince Myshkin, bringing readers face-to-face with human suffering and spiritual compassion.

440542 624pp £5.99

Netochka Nezvanova

Translated with an introduction by Jane Kentish

Written as a serial, this never-completed first publication introduces many of the themes that dominate Dostoyevsky's later great novels.

444556 176pp £6.99

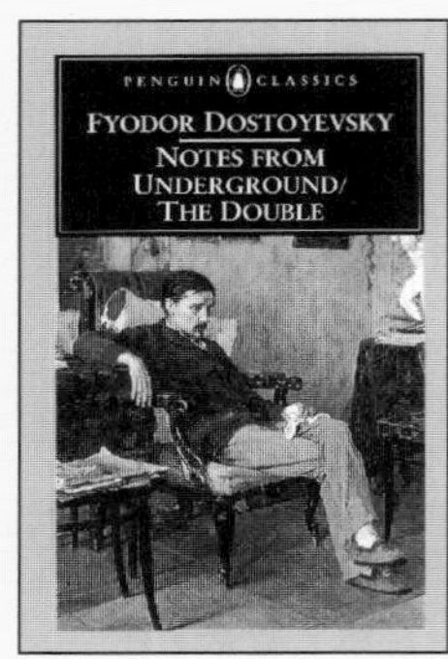

Notes from Underground
The Double

Translated with an introduction by
Jessie Coulson

In *Notes from the Underground*, Dostoyevsky portrays a nihilist who probes into the dark underside of man's nature: *The Double* is a classic study of psychological breakdown.

442529 288pp £4.99

Poor Folk and Other Stories

Translated with an introduction by
David McDuff

Dostoyevsky's first great literary triumph, the novella *Poor Folk* is presented here along with 'The Landlady', 'Mr Prokharchin' and 'Polzunkov'.

445056 288pp £6.99

Uncle's Dream and Other Stories

Translated with an introduction by
David McDuff

Completed after four years of Siberian exile, *Uncle's Dream* is remarkable for its uncharacteristic objectivity, satire, and even farce, revealing a profound transformation in the author's worldview. In addition, this edition includes the stories 'A Weak Heart', 'White Nights' and 'The Meek Girl'.

445188 304pp £6.99

The Village of Stepanchikovo

Translated with an introduction by
Ignat Avsey

This work introduces a Dostoyevsky unfamiliar to most readers, revealing his unexpected talents as a humorist and satirist. While its light-hearted tone and amusing plot make it a joy to read, it also contains the prototypes of characters who appear in his later works.

446583 224pp £5.99

NIKOLAI GOGOL

1809–1852

Dead Souls

Translated with an introduction by
David Magarshack

In *Dead Souls* Gogol set out 'to solve the riddle of my existence'. The first part took eight years to write. It introduces Chichikov, 'a businessman who buys up the dead souls' or serfs whose names still appear on the government census. He is a phoney committing phantom crimes, dealing in paper ghosts, and the most devilish and beguiling product of Gogol's inspiration.

441131 384pp £8.99

Diary of a Madman and Other Stories

Translated with an introduction by
Ronald Wilks

These five stories, 'Diary of a Madman', 'The Overcoat', 'How Ivan Ivanovich Quarrelled with Ivan Nikiforovich', 'Ivan Fyodorovich Shponka and His Aunt' and 'The Nose', demonstrate Gogol's peculiar and strikingly original imagination.

442731 192pp £5.99

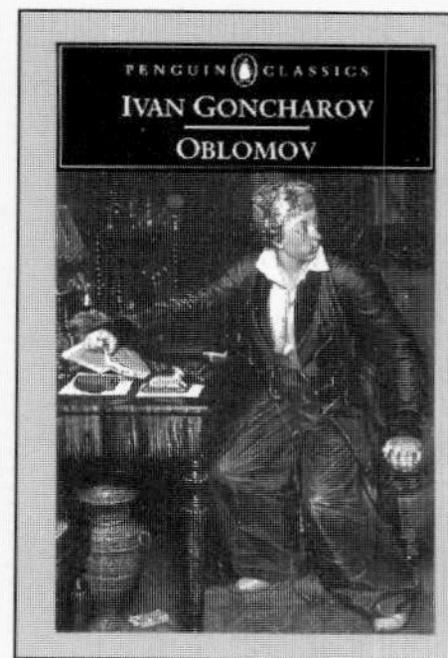

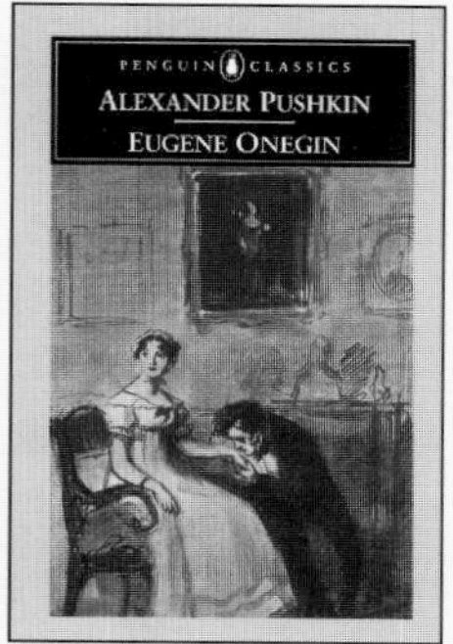

IVAN GONCHAROV

1812–1891

OBLOMOV

Translated with an introduction by
David Magarshack

Goncharov's detached yet sympathetic portrait of the humdrum life of his ineffectual and slothful hero is a tragicomedy created through painstaking accumulation of seemingly insignificant details alongside a sympathetic analysis of his character.

440402 496pp £7.99

THE GOVERNMENT INSPECTOR AND OTHER RUSSIAN PLAYS

Translated with an introduction by
Joshua Cooper

This collection includes *The Infant* by Fonvizin, *Chatsky* by Griboyedov, *The Government Inspector* by Gogol and *Thunder* by Ostrovsky. Together, these plays constitute some of the golden moments in Russian theatre before Chekhov.

44579X 400pp £8.99

MIKHAIL LERMONTOV

1814–1841

A HERO OF OUR TIME

Translated with an introduction by
Paul Foote

Lermontov's portrait of a cynical, flamboyant man influenced Tolstoy, Dostoyevsky, Chekhov and other nineteenth-century masters.

44176X 192pp £5.99

NIKOLAI LESKOV

1831–1895

LADY MACBETH OF MTSENSK DISTRICT AND OTHER STORIES

Translated by with an introduction
David McDuff

A pervasive religious spirit combined with lurid dashes of intrigue and carefully detailed descriptions of nineteenth-century peasant life characterize Leskov's work. This selection includes 'The Sealed Angel', 'Pamphalon the Entertainer', 'Musk-Ox' and 'A Winter's Day'.

444912 432pp £8.99

ALEXANDER PUSHKIN

1799–1837

EUGENE ONEGIN

Translated by Charles Johnston with an
introduction by John Bayley

Hailed by critics as the finest English-language rendering ever achieved, Charles Johnston's verse translation of *Eugene Onegin* captures the lyric intensity and gusto of Pushkin's incomparable poem.

443940 240pp £6.99

THE QUEEN OF SPADES AND OTHER STORIES

Translated with an introduction by
Rosemary Edmonds

Known as Russia's greatest poet, Pushkin was equally at ease working in other literary forms. The prose collected here includes 'The Captain's Daughter', which chronicles the Pugachev Rebellion of 1770, 'The Negro of Peter the Great' and 'Dubrovsky'.

441190 320pp £6.99

Tales of Belkin and Other Prose Writings

Translated by Ronald Wilks with an introduction by John Bayley

Pushkin was the writer, according to Dostoyevsky, who 'showed us a whole gallery of genuinely beautiful Russian characters which he discovered in the Russian people'. Alongside the *Tales*, this new Penguin Classic contains a selection of his other writings, including the novel fragment 'Roslavlev', 'Egyptian Nights' and Pushkin's autobiographical 'Journey to Arzrum'.

446753 224pp £7.99

LEO TOLSTOY

1828–1910

Anna Karenin

Translated with an introduction by Rosemary Edmonds

Tolstoy's intense, imaginative insight is brilliantly apparent in this psychological novel and its portraits of the passionate Anna, Count Vronsky, and Levin, who may be seen as a reflection of Tolstoy himself.

440410 864pp £4.99

Childhood, Boyhood, Youth

Translated with an introduction by Rosemary Edmonds

These sketches, a mixture of fact and fiction, provide an expressive self-portrait of the young Tolstoy and hints of the man and writer he would become.

441395 320pp £7.99

A Confession and Other Religious Writings

Translated with an introduction by Jane Kentish

Tolstoy's passionate and iconoclastic writings – on issues of faith, immortality, freedom, violence and morality – reflect his intellectual search for truth and a religion firmly grounded in reality. The selection includes 'A Confession', 'Religion and Morality', 'What is Religion, and of What Does Its Essence Consist?' and 'The Law of Love and the Law of Violence'.

444734 240pp £6.99

The Death of Ivan Ilyich and Other Stories

Translated with an introduction by Rosemary Edmonds

The Death of Ivan Ilyich is a magnificent story of a spiritual awakening. 'The Cossacks' tells of a disenchanted nobleman who finds happiness amid the simple people of the Caucasus; and 'Happily Ever After' traces the maturing of romantic love into 'family attachment'.

445080 336pp £5.99

How Much Land Does a Man Need? and Other Stories

Edited with an introduction by A N Wilson

Translated by Ronald Wilks

These short works, ranging from Tolstoy's earliest tales to the brilliant title story, are rich in the insights and passion that characterize all of his explorations of love, war, courage and civilization.

445064 256pp £6.99

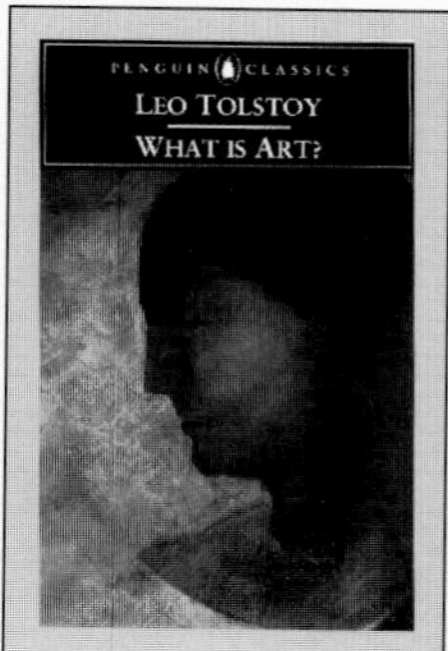

The Kreutzer Sonata and Other Stories

Translated with an introduction by David McDuff

These four tales – the title story plus 'The Devil', 'The Forged Coupon' and 'After the Ball' – embody the moral, religious and existential themes of Tolstoy's final creative period.

444696 288pp £6.99

Master and Man and Other Stories

Translated with an introduction by Paul Foote

Written in the 1890s, both 'Master and Man' and 'Father Sergius' are preoccupied with material desires – for the flesh in one instance and for money in the other. In 'Hadji Murat', Tolstoy offers a precisely written and memorable portrait of a treacherous soldier.

443312 272pp £6.99

Resurrection

Translated with an introduction by Rosemary Edmonds

In this story of a fallen man and an emphatically non-Christian 'resurrection', Tolstoy writes a compelling tale of the underworld and turns a highly critical eye on the law, the penal system and the Church.

441840 576pp £6.99

The Sebastopol Sketches

Translated with an introduction by David McDuff

These three short stories stem from Tolstoy's military experience during the Crimean War.

444688 192pp £5.99

War and Peace

Translated with an introduction by Rosemary Edmonds

This epic presents a complete tableau of Russian society during the great Napoleonic Wars, from 1805 to 1815.

444173 1472pp £7.99

What is Art?

Translated by Richard Pevear and Larissa Volokhonsky, with a preface by Richard Pevear

This profound analysis of the nature of art is the culmination of a series of essays and polemics on issues of morality, social justice and religion. Considering and rejecting the idea that art reveals and reinvents through beauty, Tolstoy perceives the question of the nature of art to be a religious one. Ultimately, he concludes, art must be a force for good, for the progress and improvement of mankind.

446427 240pp £7.99

IVAN TURGENEV

1818–1883

Fathers and Sons

Translated with an introduction by Rosemary Edmonds

This powerful novel resounds with a recognition of the universal clash between generations, in this instance localized in the hostility between the reactionary 1840s and the revolutionary 1860s. Included is the 1970 Romanes lecture 'Fathers and Children' by Isaiah Berlin.

441476 304pp £4.99

First Love

Translated by Isaiah Berlin with an introduction by V S Pritchett

Isaiah Berlin's translation reproduces in finely wrought English the original story's simplicity, lyricism and sensitivity.

443355 112pp £4.99

Home of the Gentry

Translated by Richard Freeborn

Through the story of one man, Turgenev describes a whole generation of Russians who discover the emptiness of European ideas and long for a reconciliation with their homeland.

442243 208pp £5.99

A Month in the Country

Translated with an introduction by Isaiah Berlin

Turgenev's most celebrated play, written in 1850, is a tragicomedy exploring that most universal theme, the love triangle.

44436X 128pp £4.99

On the Eve

Translated with an introduction by Gilbert Gardiner

A love story with a tragic ending, this novel portrays the everyday life of a Russian country estate during the mid-nineteenth century.

440097 240pp £5.99

Rudin

Edited and translated by Richard Freeborn

Rudin, the hero of Turgenev's first novel, is in part an example of the banality of the Russian intelligentsia of the 1840s, in part a hero with the charms and failings of Don Quixote.

443045 192pp £6.99

Sketches from a Hunter's Album

Translated with an introduction by Richard Freeborn

First published in 1852, Turgenev's impressions of Russian peasant life and the tyranny of serfdom led to his arrest and confinement.

445226 416pp £7.99

Spring Torrents

Translated with an introduction by Leonard Schapiro

This is an exquisitely written, partly autobiographical treatment of one of Turgenev's favourite themes – man's inability to learn about love without first losing his innocence.

44369X 240pp £6.99

WORLD LITERATURE

Courtesy of Coordinator Nacional de Asuntos Jurídicos y Laborales

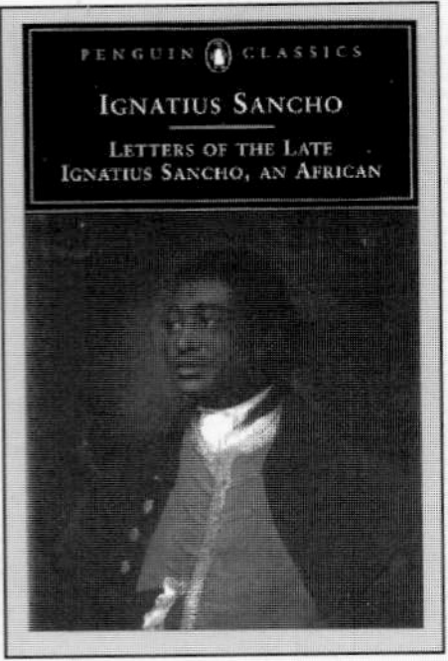

AFRICAN

OLAUDAH EQUIANO

c. 1745–1797

The Interesting Narrative and Other Writings

Edited and with an introduction by Vincent Carretta

An account of the slave trade by a native African, former slave, and loyal British subject, *The Interesting Narrative* is both an exciting, often terrifying, adventure story and an important precursor to such famous nineteenth-century slave narratives as Frederick Douglass's autobiography.

434852 400pp £6.99

IGNATIUS SANCHO

1729–1780

The Letters of the Late Ignatius Sancho, An African

Edited with an introduction by Vincent Carretta

One of the first works of literature written in English by an author of African descent.

Born on 1729 on a slave ship bound for the West Indies, Ignatius Sancho rose from servitude to become the most celebrated Afro-Briton of his time. His thoughts on race and politics – including his criticism of British imperialism in India, the complicity of Africans in the slave trade and the blatant racism that flourished around him – will be of particular interest to twentieth-century readers.

436375 384pp £7.99

OLIVE SCHREINER

1855–1920

The Story of an African Farm

Introduction by Dan Jacobson

Written by an avid feminist and political activist and first published in 1883, this masterful novel reveals much about colonial history as it tells the story of two orphaned sisters growing up on a lonely farm in a Bible-dominated area of South Africa during the 1860s.

431845 304pp £6.99

ARGENTINIAN

DOMINGO F SARMIENTO

1811–1888

Facundo: Civilization and Barbarism

Translated by Mary Peabody Mann with an introduction by Ilan Stavans

Now considered the most important Latin American essay of the nineteenth century, *Facundo* first appeared in 1845, when Sarmiento was living in political exile from Argentina. Ostensibly a biography of the gaucho 'barbarian' Juan Facundo Quiroga, it is also a complex and passionate work of history, sociology and political commentary. This edition includes an informative introduction and a chronology of Sarmiento's life and times.

436774 288pp £7.99

NEW APRIL 99

AUSTRALIAN

MARCUS CLARKE

1846–1881

His Natural Life

Edited by Stephen Murray-Smith

Foreshadowing the nightmare vision of the twentieth century in which evil is perceived as central to the condition of man, *His Natural Life* is a novel of startling power and originality. It is the greatest novel to come out of colonial Australia and pinpoints with shocking immediacy the reality of Botany Bay and the horrors of the transportation system – a fate so awful that many convicts hanged themselves rather than suffer it.

430512 928pp £9.99

HENRY HANDEL RICHARDSON

1870–1946

The Fortunes of Richard Mahony

Introduction by Michael Ackland with an afterword by Dorothy Green

Written by a woman considered one of the best naturalistic novelists and set in the Australia of the gold-mining boom, this trilogy is one of the great classics of Australian literature. In the figure of Richard Mahony, Richardson captures the soul of the emigrant, ever restless, ever searching for some equilibrium, yet never really able to settle anywhere. Richard's search, though, is also the more universal one for a meaning that will validate and give purpose to his existence.

43710X 864pp £9.99

NEW JANUARY 99

The Getting of Wisdom

Introduction by Michael Ackland

When Laura Rambotham arrives at an exclusive Melbourne girls school from her country home, she is ridiculed by the other pupils for her differences, especially for her 'unpardonable sin', her exceptional musical ability. Described by H G Wells as the best school story he knew, *The Getting of Wisdom* is the classic Australian novel of school days, a compelling and frank account of a young girl's coming of age.

436197 264pp £7.99

NEW FEBRUARY 99

BRAZILIAN

JOACHIM MARIA MACHADO DE ASSIS

1839–1908

Dom Casmurro

Translated with an introduction by Robert Scott-Buccleuch

Bentinho, now a taciturn lawyer, looks back on his life and tells the Othello-like story of his adolescent love, their marriage, and his wife's infidelity – or so he perceives it through his passionate jealousy.

446125 224pp £6.99

MEXICAN

SOR JUANA INÉS DE LA CRUZ

1648–1695

Poems, Protest, and a Dream

Translated by Margaret Sayers Peden with an introduction by Ilan Stavans

'In the history of Spanish American literature, Sor Juana stands alone, the prodigy of the colonial period, her genius uncontested today. She is the Mexican muse, the inspiration of contemporary writers.' Margaret Sayers Peden

A unique and bilingual collection of writings by Latin America's finest baroque poet. Written in 1691 in response to her bishop's injunction against her intellectual pursuits, it is a passionate defence of the rights of women to study, to teach and to write.

447032 304pp £7.99

MEDIEVAL LITERATURE

Courtesy of Scala

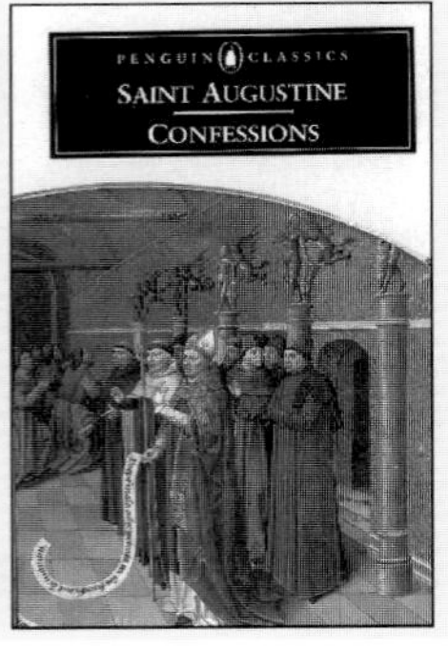

ABÉLARD AND HÉLOÏSE

c. 1079–1142

The Letters of Abélard and Héloise

Translated with an introduction by
Betty Radice

This collection of writings offers insight into the minds of two prominent Christian medieval figures – the French scholastic philosopher Peter Abélard and his beloved Héloïse, who became a learned abbess – and their celebrated but tragic love affair.

442979 320pp £8.99

ADOMNÁN OF IONA

c. 628–704

Life of St Columba

Translated with an introduction by
Richard Sharpe

This biography, written one hundred years after the death of St Columba (597) presents a richly detailed portrait of religious life in the sixth century.

444629 432pp £8.99

ANSELM OF AOSTA

1033–1109

The Prayers and Meditations of St Anselm

Translated with an introduction by
Sister Benedicta Ward

Combining personal ardour and scrupulous theology, *Prayers and Meditations* offers an intimate view of this Archbishop of Canterbury, most noted for his acceptance of rational inquiry into the mysteries of faith.

442782 288pp £7.99

THOMAS AQUINAS

c. 1225–1274

Selected Writings

Edited and translated with an introduction
by Ralph McInerny

436324 880pp £12.99

(featured in Italian Literature on page 96)

ASSER AND OTHERS

d. 910

Asser's Life of King Alfred and Other Contemporary Sources

Translated with an introduction by
Simon Keynes and Michael Lapidge

This comprehensive collection includes Asser's *Life of Alfred*, extracts from *The Anglo-Saxon Chronicle*, and Alfred's own writings, laws and will.

444092 368pp £7.99

ST AUGUSTINE

354–430

City of God

Translated by Henry Bettenson with an
introduction by John O'Meara

Augustine examines the inefficacy of the Roman gods and of human civilization in general. Blending Platonism with Christianity, he created the first Christian theology of history.

444262 1152pp £14.99

Confessions

Translated with an introduction by
R S Pine-Coffin

This autobiography is both an explanation of Augustine's own conversion to Christianity

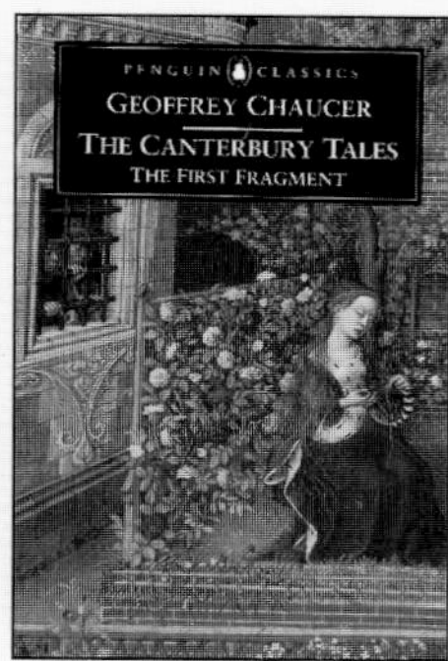

and an attempt to convince the reader that it is the one true faith.

44114X 352pp £7.99

BEDE

673–735

Ecclesiastical History of the English People

Translated by Leo Sherley-Price. Edited with a new introduction by D H Farmer

Opening with a background sketch of Roman Britain's geography and history, Bede recounts the development of the Anglo-Saxon government and religion during the formative years of the British people.

44565X 400pp £8.99

BEROUL

c. 1120

The Romance of Tristan

Translated with an introduction by Alan S Fredrick

This edition contains perhaps the earliest and most elemental version of the tragic legend of Tristan and Yseult in a distinguished prose translation.

442308 176pp £7.99

GEOFFREY CHAUCER

1343–1400

The Canterbury Tales

Translated into Modern English by Nevill Coghill

Modern verse translation of Chaucer's pilgrims' tales as they journey from Southwark to Canterbury. A bawdy, pious, erudite, comic picture of medieval English life.

440224 528pp £3.99

The Canterbury Tales: The First Fragment

Edited with an introduction and glosses by Michael Alexander

Comprised of the General Prologue and the prologues and tales of the Knight, Miller, Reeve, and Cook, this is the most widely read portion of Chaucer's masterpiece. This unique edition contains the Middle English text on one page and meticulous glosses of Chaucer's language on the facing page.

434097 320pp £5.99

Love Visions

Translated into Modern English with an introduction by Brian Stone

Spanning Chaucer's working life, these four poems move from the conventional allegorical 'love visions' toward realistic storytelling and provide a marvellous self-portrait. This selection includes 'The Book of the Duchess', 'The House of Fame', 'The Parliament of the Birds', and 'The Legend of Good Women'.

444084 272pp £7.99

Troilus and Criseyde

Translated into Modern English by Nevill Coghill

Chaucer's depiction of passionate sexual love, his grasp of tragedy, and his sense of the ridiculous hidden in the sublime are all displayed in this poetic retelling of the classical story set during the Trojan War.

442391 368pp £7.99

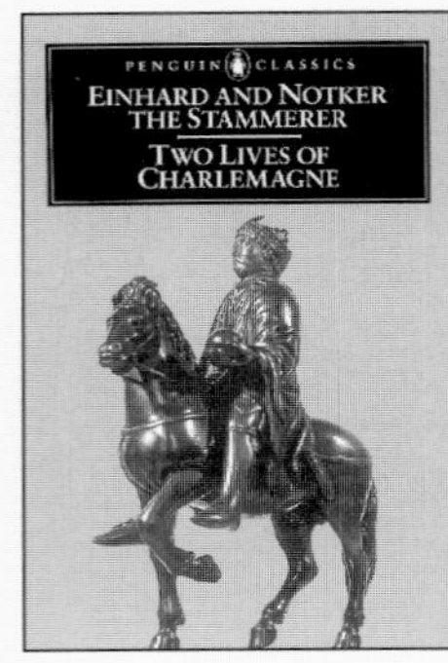

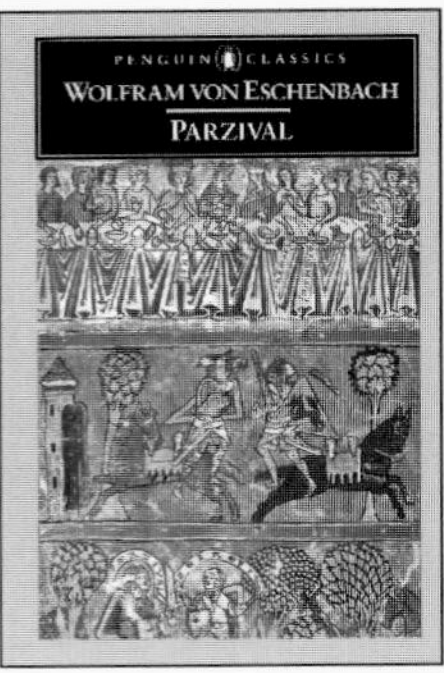

CHRÉTIEN DE TROYES

c. 1150

Arthurian Romances

Translated with an introduction by William Kibler *Erec and Enide* translated by Carleton Carroll

Fantastic adventures abound in these courtly romances: *Erec and Enide*, *Cligés*, *The Knight of the Cart*, *The Knight with the Lion* and *The Story of the Grail*.

445218 528pp £9.99

ANNA COMNENA

1083–1148

The Alexiad of Anna Comnena

Translated with an introduction by E R A Sewter

A Byzantine emperor's daughter vividly records the turbulence that marked the rule of her father, Alexius I (1081–1118).

442154 560pp £9.99

EINHARD AND NOTKER

c. 770–840

Two Lives of Charlemagne

Translated with an introduction by Lewis Thorpe

Einhard offers a factual account of Charlemagne's personal life and his achievements in warfare, learning, art and statesmanship, while Notker's anecdotal approach presents Charlemagne as a near-legendary figure.

442138 240pp £7.99

WOLFRAM VON ESCHENBACH

c. 1195–1225

Parzival

Translated by A T Hatto

A prose translation of Wolfram von Eschenbach's thirteenth-century narrative poem re-creates and completes the story of the Holy Grail, left unfinished by Chrétien de Troyes.

443614 448pp £9.99

EUSEBIUS

265–340

The History of the Church

Translated by G A Williamson
Edited and revised with an introduction by Andrew Louth

A clear, readable translation of the ten books of Bishop Eusebius's *Ecclesiastical History* – the only surviving record of the Church during its crucial first three hundred years – this edition recounts the martyrdoms, heresies, schisms and proceedings that led to Nicaea and other great church councils.

445358 480pp £8.99

JEAN FROISSART

c. 1337–1410

Chronicles

Selected and translated with an introduction by Geoffrey Brereton

This selection from Froissart's *Chronicles* forms a vast panorama of Europe, from the deposition of Edward II to the downfall of Richard II.

442006 496pp £8.99

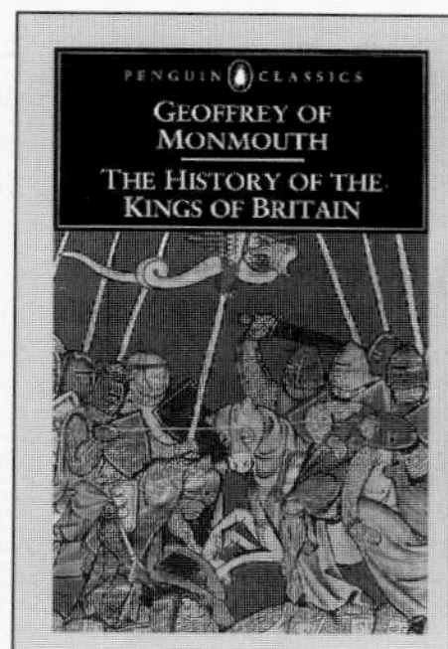

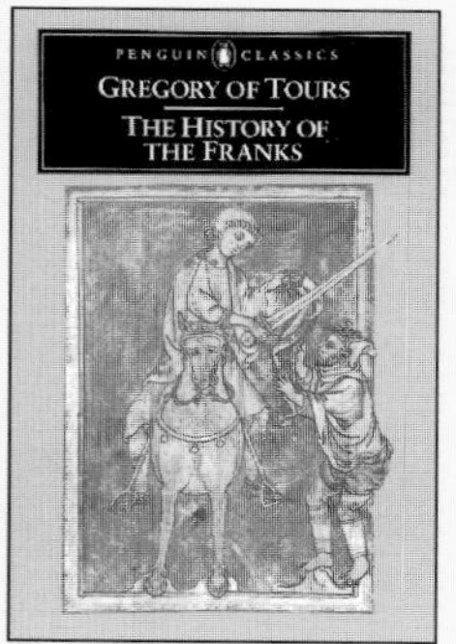

GEOFFREY OF MONMOUTH

d. 1155

The History of the Kings of Britain

Translated with an introduction by Lewis Thorpe

This heroic epic of the twelfth century, describing such half-legendary kings as Cymbeline, Arthur and Lear, inspired Malory, Spenser, Shakespeare and many other writers.

441700 384pp £8.99

GERALD OF WALES

c. 1146–1223

History and Topography of Ireland

Translated with an introduction by John J O'Meara

Arguably the most authoritative primary source for what is known about medieval Ireland, this lively history by a twelfth-century Norman describes the land's topography, natural resources and inhabitants in vivid detail.

444238 144pp £6.99

The Journey Through Wales
The Description of Wales

Translated with an introduction by Lewis Thorpe

The Journey, an accurate and comprehensive history of twelfth-century Wales, is filled with lively anecdotes and folklore; *The Description* offers a fascinating picture of the life of ordinary Welsh people.

443398 336pp £8.99

GOTTFRIED VON STRASSBURG

c. 1210

Tristan

Translated with an introduction by A T Hatto

This medieval version of the legendary romance between Tristan and Isolde portrays Tristan as a sophisticated pre-Renaissance man.

440984 384pp £8.99

GREGORY OF TOURS

c. 540–594

The History of the Franks

Translated with an introduction by Lewis Thorpe

This colourful narrative of French history in the sixth century is a dramatic and detailed portrait of a period of political and religious turmoil.

442952 720pp £12.00

ROBERT HENRYSON

c. 1424–1506

The Testament of Cresseid and Other Poems

Selected by Hugh MacDiarmid

This collection of fifteenth-century poems features Henryson's pendant to *Troilus and Criseyde*, notable for its controversial moralization and tragic interpretation of Chaucer's poem.

445072 96pp £5.99

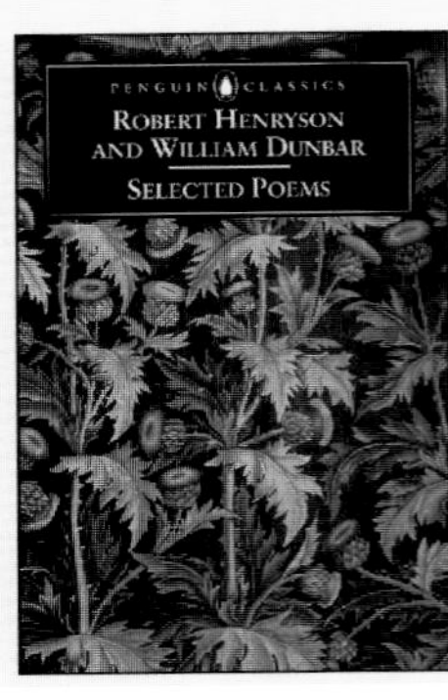

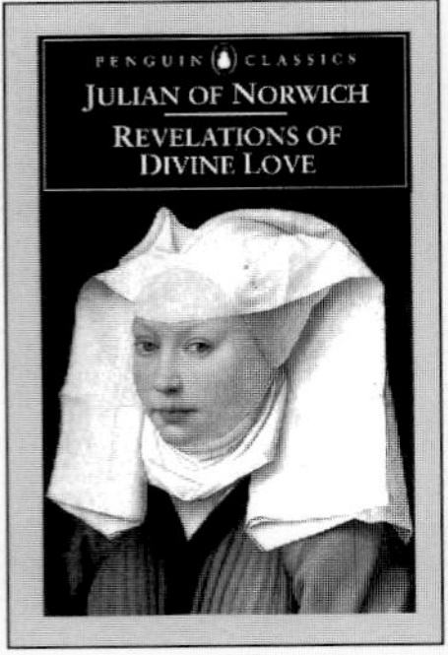

ROBERT HENRYSON AND WILLIAM DUNBAR

c. 1424–1506 c. 1420–1513

SELECTED POEMS

Edited by Douglas Gray

Robert Henryson and William Dunbar are the most powerful and individual voices in the Scottish poetry of the Middle Ages. Both were influenced by Chaucer and fascinated by the frailty of human life, relations between men and women, and the Christian hope of salvation.

42248X 432pp £8.99

NEW OCTOBER 98

WALTER HILTON

d. 1396

THE LADDER OF PERFECTION

Translated by Leo Sherley-Price with an introduction by Clifton Wolters

A superb example of medieval mystical prose, this fourteenth-century doctrine on the pursuit of spiritual salvation through religious contemplation continues to inspire with its language of pure and simple beauty.

445110 288pp £7.99

ST IGNATIUS OF LOYOLA

1491–1556

PERSONAL WRITINGS

Translated with introductions by Joseph A Munitiz and Philip Endean

The founder of the Jesuit order, Ignatius Loyola was one of the most influential figures of the Counter-Reformation. The works in this volume – *Reminiscences*, *The Spiritual Diary*, *The Spiritual Exercises* and selected letters – shed light on the more private aspects of Ignatius's life and beliefs.

433856 448pp £9.99

JEAN DE JOINVILLE AND GEOFFROI DE VILLEHARDOUIN

b. 1224 1150–1218

CHRONICLES OF THE CRUSADES

Translated with an introduction by M R B Shaw

These two famous Old French chronicles were composed by soldiers who took part in the Holy Wars and offer both eyewitness accounts of the battles and pictures of life in the East.

441247 368pp £8.99

JULIAN OF NORWICH

c. 1342–1416

REVELATIONS OF DIVINE LOVE

Translated by Elizabeth Spearing, with an introduction by A C Spearing

This account of the sixteen visions of Mother Julian of Norwich and her meditations on her mystical experience expresses profound theology in simple language.

446737 240pp £7.99

NEW AUGUST 98

MARGERY KEMPE

c. 1373–1439

THE BOOK OF MARGERY KEMPE

Translated with an introduction by
Barry Windeatt

This earliest-known British autobiography is a remarkable and touching record of the author's difficult pilgrimage from madness to Christian faith.

432515 336pp £7.99

WILLIAM LANGLAND

c. 1330–1386

PIERS THE PLOUGHMAN

Translated with an introduction by
J F Goodridge

Written by a fourteenth-century cleric, this spiritual allegory explores man in relation to his ultimate destiny against the background of teeming, colourful medieval life.

440879 320pp £4.99

SIR THOMAS MALORY

c. 1435–1471

LE MORTE D'ARTHUR

Edited by Janet Cowen and with an introduction by John Lawlor

One of the most readable and moving accounts of the Knights of the Round Table, this version of the Arthurian legend was edited and first published by William Caxton in 1485.

Volume 1

430431 528pp £7.99

Volume 2

43044X 560pp £7.99

MARIE DE FRANCE

c. 1180

THE LAIS OF MARIE DE FRANCE

Translated with an introduction by
Glyn S Burgess and Keith Busby

Twelve short story-poems, based on Breton tales of love in crisis, are presented in plain prose translations as close to the twelfth-century original as possible. The volume includes the Old French text of *Laüstic*.

444769 144pp £6.99

CHRISTINE DE PISAN

b. 1365

THE TREASURE OF THE CITY OF LADIES OR THE BOOK OF THREE VIRTUES

Translated with an introduction by
Sarah Lawson

A valuable counterbalance to chronicles of medieval life written by men, this 1405 'survival manual' addresses all women, from those at the royal court to prostitutes, and portrays their lives in fine and often wry detail.

44453X 192pp £6.99

MICHAEL PSELLUS

1018–1096

FOURTEEN BYZANTINE RULERS

Translated with an introduction by
E R A Sewter

This chronicle of the Byzantine Empire, beginning in 1025, shows a profound understanding of the power politics that characterized the empire and led to its decline.

441697 400pp £8.99

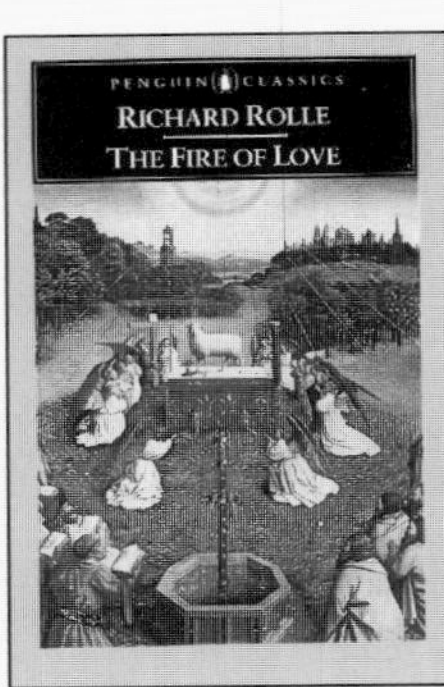

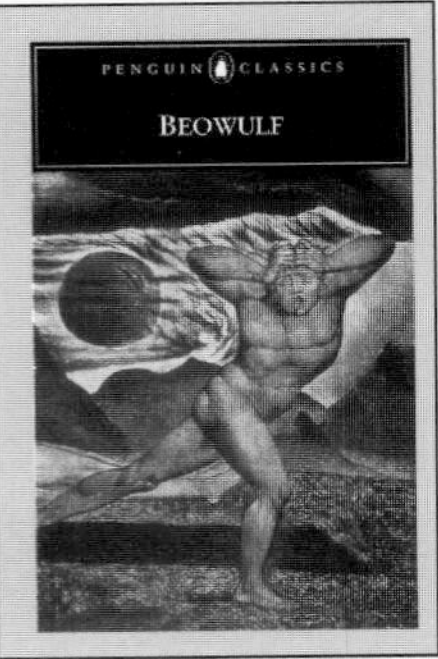

RICHARD ROLLE

c. 1300–1349

The Fire of Love

Translated with an introduction by
Clifton Wolters

Part autobiography and part practical guide to the devout life, *The Fire of Love* is an intense document of the fourteenth-century mystic's love of God.

442561 192pp £6.99

THOMAS À KEMPIS

1380–1471

The Imitation of Christ

Translated with an introduction by
Leo Sherley-Price

One of the most-read and influential of Christian classics, this is a seminal work of the Devotio Moderna, the late-medieval reform movement that returned to the original Apostolic zeal and simplicity of Christianity.

440275 224pp £6.99

JACOBUS DE VORAGINE

c. 1229–1298

The Golden Legend: Selections

Selected and translated by Christopher Stace, with an introduction by
Richard Hamer

The Golden Legend is one of the central texts of the Middle Ages, a superb summary of saints' lives and religious festivals which decisively influenced the imagery of poetry, painting and stained glass.

446486 432pp £8.99

NEW SEPTEMBER 98

ANONYMOUS

ANCRENE WISSE

Guide for Anchoresses

Translated with an introduction by
Hugh White

This classic of devotional literature, one of the great prose works of the Middle Ages, looks at the practices of women entering a life of solitary prayer, meditation and ascetic religion.

445854 272pp £7.99

BEOWULF

c. 700

A Verse Translation

Translated with an introduction by
Michael Alexander

This heroic Old English poem, perhaps the most significant work to survive from the Anglo-Saxon period, is rendered in an eloquent verse translation.

442685 176pp £5.99

BEOWULF

Edited with an introduction, notes and a glossary by Michael Alexander

The Anglo-Saxon verse text on the left-hand page is faced by a page on which almost every word is glossed. In addition, succinct footnotes clarify historical and cultural matters.

433775 272pp £7.99

THE BOOK OF DEDE KORKUT

Translated with an introduction by
Geoffrey Lewis

Twelve stories set in the heroic age of the Oghuz Turks combine elements of nomadic society with later Islamic culture, bringing to life an untamed civilization and its bizarre and unforgettable characters.

442987 224pp £7.99

THE CLOUD OF UNKNOWING AND OTHER WORKS

Translated with an introduction by
Clifton Wolters

This devotional classic from the fourteenth century includes three shorter works attributed to the same writer – *The Epistle of Privy Counsel*, *Dionysius's Mystical Training (Deonise Hid Divinite)*, and *The Epistle of Prayer* – illuminating the close relationship between medieval spirituality and mysticism.

443851 240pp £7.99

THE DEATH OF KING ARTHUR

Translated with an introduction by
James Cable

Set in the twilight of the Arthurian world, this French medieval romance tells of Lancelot's adultery with Guinevere, the arrival of the treacherous Mordred, and the deaths of both Arthur and Lancelot.

442553 240pp £7.99

THE EXETER BOOK OF RIDDLES

Revised edition

Translated with an introduction by
Kevin Crossley-Holland

The eleventh-century manuscript of Old English verses, kept in Exeter Cathedral, is one of the most famous treasures of the medieval period. These ninety-six riddles cover a wide range of subjects – from storms at sea to animal life, from weaponry to music and writing – and are full of sharp observation and wit.

433678 144pp £6.99

KING ARTHUR'S DEATH

MORTE ARTHURE/LE MORTE ARTHUR

Translated and with introductions by
Brian Stone

Modern verse translations of two Midlands Arthurian epics provide a vivid contrast of medieval poetic tone and narrative style: the alliterative *Morte Arthure* (Northeast Midlands, c. 1400) and the stanzaic *Le Morte Arthur* (Northwest Midlands, c. 1350).

444459 320pp £7.99

THE MABINOGION

Translated with an introduction by
Jeffrey Gantz

These tales from the Welsh oral tradition were first written down in the thirteenth century and remain an alluring combination of fact and fantasy, myth, history and folklore.

443223 320pp £7.99

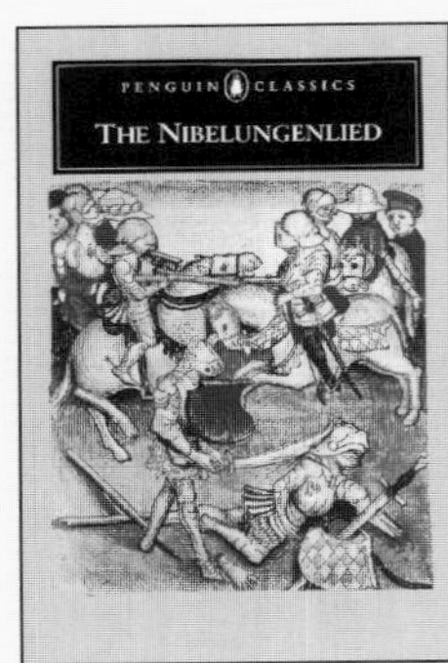

THE NIBELUNGENLIED

Translated with an introduction by A T Hatto

This great German epic poem, written during the thirteenth century, is the principal literary source of Richard Wagner's *The Ring*.

441379 416pp £8.99

THE POEM OF THE CID

Translated by Rita Hamilton and Janet Perry with an introduction by Ian Michael

This epic poem, the only one to have survived from medieval Spain, depicts the career of the warlord El Cid in a unique blend of fiction and historical fact. Both English and Spanish texts are provided.

444467 256pp £7.99

THE QUEST OF THE HOLY GRAIL

Translated with an introduction by P M Matarasso

This classic thirteenth-century tale of chivalrous adventures was intended as an allegory of man's perilous search for the grace of God.

442200 304pp £7.99

SIR GAWAIN AND THE GREEN KNIGHT

Edited by J A Burrow

Written in the latter part of the fourteenth century, this subtle and accomplished poem is roughly contemporary with *The Canterbury Tales*, though written in a more provincial dialect. The aim of this edition has been to remove unnecessary impediments while retaining the integrity of the original.

422951 176pp £6.99

SIR GAWAIN AND THE GREEN KNIGHT

Translated with an introduction by Brian Stone

This masterpiece of medieval alliterative poetry by an unknown fourteenth-century author is both magical and human, full of drama and descriptive beauty.

440925 192pp £5.99

THE SONG OF ROLAND

Translated with an introduction by Glynn Burgess

Chronicling the massacre in AD 778 of Charlemagne's army at Roncesvalles, this age-old French epic transforms a legendary defeat into an allegorical clash between Christianity and paganism.

445323 224pp £7.99

COLLECTIONS

THE AGE OF BEDE

Translated by J F Webb and D H Farmer and edited with an introduction by D H Farmer

Four of the finest medieval hagiographies provide valuable insight into the religious life and thought of the period. This collection includes *The Voyage of St Brendan*, Bede's *Life of Cuthbert*, *Lives of the Abbots of Wearmouth and Jarrow*, and Eddius Stephanus's *Life of Wilfrid*.

44727X 288pp £7.99

A CELTIC MISCELLANY

Selected and translated by Kenneth Hurlstone Jackson

More than 240 thematically arranged selections of Celtic poetry and prose, translated from the Welsh, Irish, and Scottish Gaelic and the Cornish, Breton, and Manx languages, provide insight into the Celtic mind from the earliest times to the nineteenth century.

442472 352pp £8.99

THE CISTERCIAN WORLD

Monastic Writings of the Twelfth Century

Edited and translated with an introduction by Pauline Matarasso

Collected in this volume are letters, sermons, biographies, satires and stories by the influential abbot St Bernard of Clairvaux and other monks of the Cistercian Order – a medieval order devoted to strict asceticism and a life of poverty.

433562 352pp £8.99

THE EARLIEST ENGLISH POEMS

Third Revised Edition

Translated with an introduction by Michael Alexander

This select volume includes translations of heroic poems (including the oldest poem in the English language), a passage from Beowulf, 'riddles' from *The Exeter Book*, and elegies in Anglo-Saxon metre and alliteration.

445943 192pp £7.99

EARLY CHRISTIAN LIVES

Athanasius: Life of Antony

Jerome: Life of Paul of Thebes/Life of Hilarion/Life of Malchus

Sulpicius Severus: Life of Martin of Tours

Gregory the Great: Life of Benedict

Translated and edited by Carolinne White

These pioneering *Lives* are central sources for the major Christian monastic figures from St Antony, who died in 356, to St Benedict (*c.* 480–547). They shed equal light on the beliefs and values of their celebrated authors. Full of vivid incidents and astonishing miracles, all these works proved hugely popular and influential, and also inspired much of the visual imagery of the Middle Ages.

435263 288pp £7.99

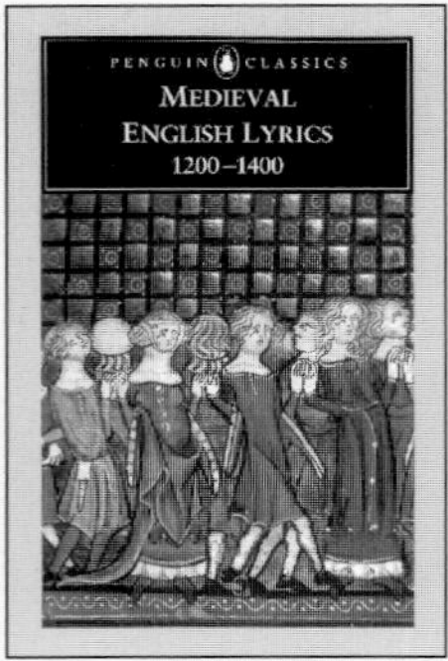

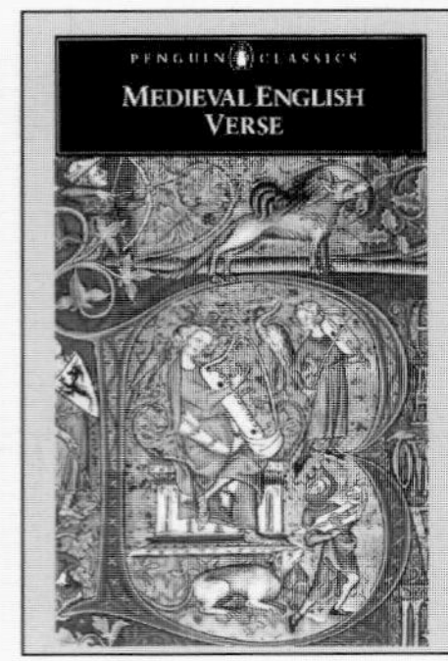

EARLY CHRISTIAN WRITINGS

The Apostolic Fathers

Translated by Maxwell Staniforth
and revised by Andrew Louth

These letters and short theological treatises provide a rich guide to the emerging traditions and organization of the infant Church.

444750 208pp £7.99

MEDIEVAL ENGLISH LYRICS

Edited with an introduction by
Thomas G Duncan

Edited anew from the original manuscripts, this collection includes the first lyrics in English to celebrate love and romantic devotion to a woman; devotional lyrics in praise of Christ and the Virgin Mary; poems on moral and penitential themes; and a variety of drinking and dancing songs, ballads, satires and poems of wit, humour and sexual innuendo.

434437 320pp £7.99

MEDIEVAL ENGLISH VERSE

Edited and translated with an introduction
by Brian Stone

Short narrative poems, religious and secular lyrics, and moral, political and comic verses are all included in this comprehensive collection of works from the thirteenth and fourteenth centuries.

441441 256pp £7.99

SAGAS

Courtesy of Carl Löfman/Promedia

SAGAS

BEOWULF

c. 700

A Verse Translation

Translated with an introduction by Michael Alexander

This heroic Old English poem, perhaps the most significant work to survive from the Anglo-Saxon period, is rendered in an eloquent verse translation.

442685 176pp £5.99

BEOWULF

Edited with an introduction, notes and a glossary by Michael Alexander

The Anglo-Saxon verse text on the left-hand page is faced by a page on which almost every word is glossed. In addition, succinct footnotes clarify historical and cultural matters.

433775 272pp £7.99

EARLY IRISH MYTHS AND SAGAS

Translated with an introduction by Jeffrey Gantz

These fourteen myths and tales, probably first written down around the eighth century AD, represent the oral tradition of Iron Age Celts who flourished in Europe during the seven centuries before Christ.

443975 288pp £7.99

EGIL'S SAGA

Translated with an introduction by Hermann Pálsson and Paul Edwards

Thought to have been written in 1230, *Egil's Saga* chronicles the histories of the ruling clans of Iceland and Norway, giving a wide-ranging view of the Viking world in the ninth and tenth centuries.

443215 256pp £6.99

EYRBYGGJA SAGA

Translated with an introduction by Hermann Pálsson and Paul Edwards

This saga dramatizes a thirteenth-century view of the past, from the pagan anarchy of the Viking Age to the settlement of Iceland, the coming of Christianity, and the beginnings of organized society.

445307 192pp £7.99

HRAFNKEL'S SAGA AND OTHER ICELANDIC STORIES

Translated with an introduction by Hermann Pálsson

These seven stories, dating from the thirteenth century, combine pagan elements and Christian ethics; some are set in the pastoral society of Iceland, while others are concerned with the royal courts of Norway and Denmark.

442383 144pp £6.99

LAXDAELA SAGA

Translated with an introduction by Magnus Magnusson and Hermann Pálsson

This dynastic chronicle, composed around 1245, sweeps across 150 years of Iceland's early history.

442189 272pp £7.99

THE MABINOGION

Translated with an introduction by Jeffrey Gantz

These tales from the Welsh oral tradition were first written down in the thirteenth century and remain an alluring combination of fact and fantasy, myth, history and folklore.

443223 320pp £7.99

THE NIBELUNGENLIED

Translated with an introduction by A T Hatto

This great German epic poem, written during the thirteenth century, is the principal literary source of Richard Wagner's *The Ring*.

441379 416pp £8.99

NJAL'S SAGA

Translated with an introduction by Magnus Magnusson and Hermann Pálsson

Based on historical events in tenth century Iceland, this spare, simple narrative describes a fifty-year blood feud from its violent beginnings to its tragic end.

441034 384pp £8.99

ORKNEYINGA SAGA

The History of the Earls of Orkney

Translated with an introduction by Hermann Pálsson and Paul Edwards

Describing the conquest of the Islands of Orkney by the Kings of Norway, this is the only medieval Norse chronicle concerned with what is now part of the British Isles.

443835 256pp £7.99

THE SAGA OF KING HROLF KRAKI

Translated with an introduction by Jesse L Byock

Although composed in fourteenth-century Iceland, Hrolf's Saga looks back to 'ancient times', long before the country was colonized by the Norsemen, when the warrior chieftain King Hrolf ruled in Denmark. A powerful human drama complete with many exciting events and stirring battle scenes, this Saga ranks among the masterworks of the Middle Ages.

43593X 144pp £7.99

NEW JULY 98

SEVEN VIKING ROMANCES

Translated with an introduction by Hermann Pálsson and Paul Edwards

Incorporating local myths and legends, as well as sources from Homer to French romances, these medieval stories feature famous kings, difficult gods and great adventures.

444742 304pp £7.99

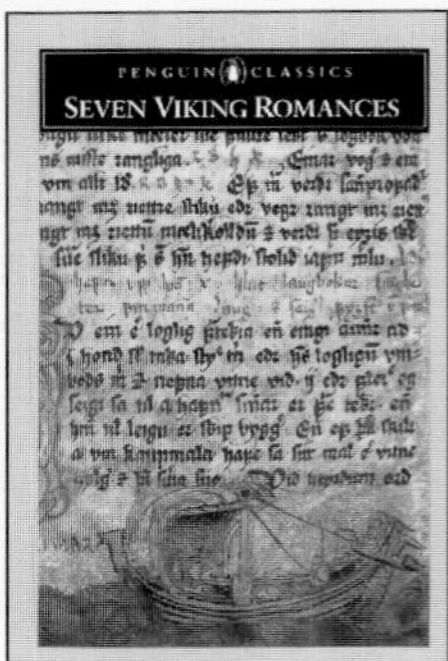

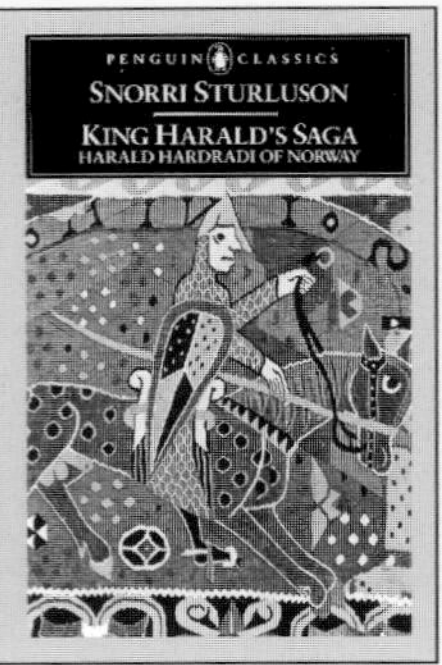

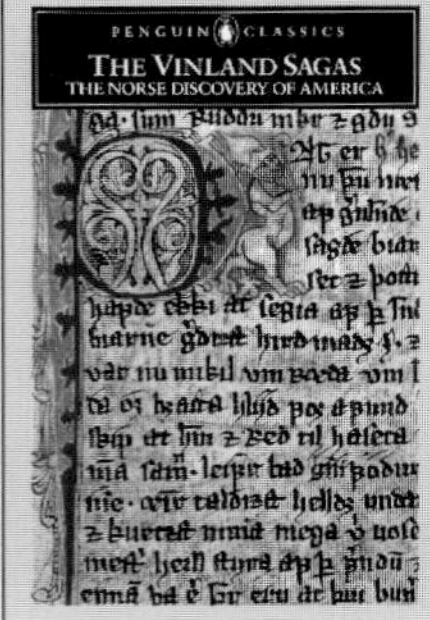

SNORRI STURLUSON

1179–1241

KING HARALD'S SAGA

Translated with an introduction by Magnus Magnusson and Hermann Pálsson

The biography of one of the most remarkable and memorable of the medieval kings of Norway, this saga culminates in the conflict between Norway and England in 1066.

441832 192pp £7.99

THE VINLAND SAGA AND THE NORSE DISCOVERY OF AMERICA

Translated by Magnus Magnusson and Hermann Pálsson

These two Icelandic sagas tell the arresting stories of the discovery of North America five centuries before the arrival of Christopher Columbus.

441549 128pp £5.99

EASTERN

LITERATURE

Courtesy of National Museum, New Delhi

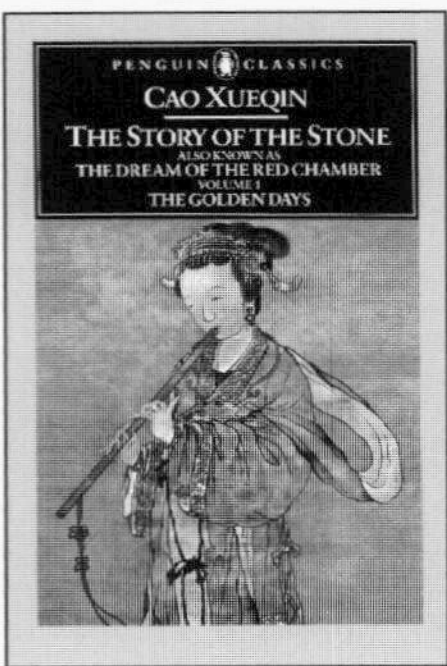

FARID UD-DIN ATTAR

c. 1142–1220

The Conference of the Birds

Translated with an introduction by
Afkham Darbandi and Dick Davis

Consisting of a group of stories bound together by a pilgrimage, this great twelfth-century poem is an allegorical rendering of the *Way of the Sufi* – the secretive and paradoxical form of Islamic mysticism.

444343 240pp £7.99

BASHO

1644–1694

The Narrow Road to the Deep North and Other Travel Sketches

Translated with an introduction by
Nobuyuki Yuasa

Basho's haiku are a series of superb pictures in which whole landscapes and seasons are evoked by description of the essential details.

441859 176pp £6.99

On Love and Barley

Haiku of Basho

Translated with an introduction by
Lucien Stryk and with illustrations by Taiga

These 253 selections reveal Basho's mastery of the genre.

444599 96pp £5.99

CAO XUEQIN

c. 1715–1763

The Story of the Stone

Translated with an introduction by
David Hawkes

Divided into five volumes, *The Story of the Stone* charts the glory and decline of the illustrious Jia family. This novel re-creates the ritualized hurly-burly of Chinese family life that would otherwise have been lost and infuses it with affirming Buddhist belief.

Volume 1 The Golden Days

442936 544pp £11.00

Volume 2 The Crab-Flower Club

443266 608pp £10.99

Volume 3 The Warning Voice

443703 640pp £11.00

Volume 4 The Debt of Tears

Translated with an introduction by
John Minford

443711 400pp £11.00

Volume 5 The Dream Wakes

Translated with an introduction by
John Minford

44372X 384pp £9.99

CONFUCIUS

551–479 BC

The Analects

Translated with an introduction by D C Lau

The only reliable account of the philosophy of the legendary Chinese sage, the *Lun-yü* (*Analects*) constitute a collection of Confucius's sayings compiled by his pupils shortly after his death.

443487 256pp £7.99

OMAR KHAYYÁM

1048–1122

The Ruba'iyat of Omar Khayyam

Translated with an introduction and notes by Peter Avery and John Heath-Stubbs

Philosopher, mathematician, poet and astronomer, Omar Khayyám is known and loved throughout the world for his celebrated *Ruba'iyat*. This contemporary edition of Khayyám has been selected and translated by Persian scholar Peter Avery and poet John Heath-Stubbs.

443843 128pp £5.99

LAO TZU

c. 6th century BC

Tao Te Ching 🎧

Translated with an introduction by D C Lau

The principal classic in the thought of Taoism is a treatise on both personal conduct and government that advances a philosophy of meekness as the surest path to survival.

44131X 176pp £6.99

LI PO AND TU FU

701–762 / 712–770

Poems

Selected and translated with an introduction by Arthur Cooper

More than forty selections from two eighth-century poets of China cover the whole spectrum of human life and feeling.

442723 256pp £7.99

MENCIUS

c. 4th century BC

Mencius

Translated and with an introduction by D C Lau

The fullest of the four great Confucian texts, Mencius draws out the implications of the master's moral principles stressing the importance of individual conscience and the necessity for morality in personal and public life.

442286 288pp £8.99

MURASAKI SHIKIBU

c. 978–1026

The Tale of Genji

Translated with an introduction by Edward G Seidensticker

Distinguished translation of one of Japan's greatest novels. It follows the relationships through two generations of a closely linked court circle in tenth-century Kyoto.

443908 1120pp £18.99

The Diary of Lady Murasaki

Translated with an introduction by Richard Bowring

In *The Tale of Genji*, Lady Murasaki created one of the supreme classics of Japanese literature; her *Diary* offers an intimate and equally compelling picture of her life as tutor and companion to the Empress Shoshi. Spiced with anecdote, searching self-analysis and sharp sketches of a timid Empress, spineless courtiers and quarrelsome ladies-in-waiting, it reveals the underside of imperial splendour from an unexpected, utterly female point of view.

43576X 144pp £6.99

LADY SARASHINA

c. 2nd century AD

As I Crossed a Bridge of Dreams

Recollections of a Woman in Eleventh-Century Japan

Translated with an introduction by Ivan Morris

Born at the height of the Heian period, the pseudonymous Lady Sarashina reveals much about the Japanese literary tradition in this haunting self-portrait.

442820 176pp £7.99

VISNU SARMA

c. 6th century AD

The Pancatantra

Translated with an introduction by Chandra Rajan

This translation by a noted scholar of *The Pancatantra*, a work written before AD 570 as a manual for the ethical instruction of young princes, combines verse and prose in a highly readable version that remains faithful to the original work.

44596X 512pp £7.99

SEI SHONAGON

c. 1000

The Pillow Book of Sei Shonagon

Translated by Ivan Morris

Sei Shonagon was a court lady in tenth-century Japan at the height of the Heian culture. In her *Pillow Book* she notes down all the things that attract, displease or interest her in daily life. This is by far our most detailed source of factual material on the life of the time and is also a work of great literary beauty.

442367 416pp £9.99

SHEN FU

c. 18th century

Six Records of a Floating Life

Translated by Leonard Pratt and Chiang Su-Hui

This autobiographical novel, published in 1890, contains lively depictions of the powerful role of the courtesan, the arrogance of untrained officials and the formal and often strained arranged marriages in turn-of-the-century China.

444297 176pp £7.99

SOMADEVA

c. 1070

TALES FROM THE KATHASARITSAGARA

Translated with an introduction by Arshia Sattar and a foreword by Wendy Doniger

A compendium of tales passed down by generations of oral storytellers, the *Kathasaritsagara* – literally translated as 'ocean of the sea of stories' – is thought to have been compiled around 1070 for the queen of Kashmir. It brings together engaging stories of heroic adventure, love, lust, betrayal, deception and revenge in an uninhibited and bawdy celebration of life.

446982 320pp £8.99

WU CHÊNG-ÊN

1505–1580

MONKEY

Translated by Arthur Waley

Wu Ch'êng-ên wrote *Monkey* in the middle of the sixteenth century, adding to an ancient Chinese legend his own touches of delicacy and humour.

441115 352pp £7.99

ANTHOLOGIES AND ANONYMOUS WORKS

THE BHAGAVAD GITA

Translated with an introduction by Juan Mascaro

One of the most important mystical poems in the Hindu scriptures, *The Bhagavad Gita* ranks among the key religious books of the world.

441212 128pp £2.50

BUDDHIST SCRIPTURES

Selected and translated by Edward Conze

This selection of writings from the golden age of Buddhist literature (AD 100–400) focuses on texts intended for the layperson rather than for the monk and exhibits the humanity rather than the profundity of the scriptures. Passages from the *Dhammapada*, the *Buddhacarita*, the *Questions of King Milinda* and the *Tibetan Book of the Dead* are included.

440887 256pp £7.99

THE DHAMMAPADA

Translated with an introduction by Juan Mascaro

Compiled in the third century BC these aphorisms illustrate the Buddhist dhamma, or moral system, pointing out the narrow Path of Perfection that leads toward Nirvana.

442847 96pp £5.99

EPIC OF GILGAMESH

Translated with an introduction by
N K Sandars

Fifteen centuries before Homer, this Mesopotamian cycle of poems tells of Gilgamesh, the great king of Uruk, and his long and arduous journey to the spring of youth in search of immortality.

44100X 128pp £5.99

HINDU MYTHS

Translated by Wendy Doniger O'Flaherty

This selection and translation of seventy-five myths spans a wide range of Indian sources, from the serpent-slaying Indra of the Vedas to the medieval pantheon.

443061 368pp £7.99

JAPANESE NO DRAMAS

Translated with an introduction by
Royall Tyler

These twenty-four plays of mesmerising beauty fuse the spiritual and the sensual in the esoteric No art form, which combines music, dance, costume and language. The collection includes full notes and stage directions, as well as new interpretations of the plays that influenced writers such as Yeats, Pound and Brecht.

445390 384pp £9.99

THE KORAN

Translated with an introduction by
N J Dawood

This classic, authoritative translation has been revised to fully reflect the characteristic flavour and rhythm of Islam's most sacred work, following the original sequence of the Koranic suras.

445587 464pp £6.99

THE KORAN

With Parallel Arabic Text

Translated with an introduction by
N J Dawood

N J Dawood's vivid revised translation is presented with opposite-page parallel Arabic text in the traditional calligraphic style. The volume includes a comprehensive index. Large format.

445420 640pp £16.00

THE LAWS OF MANU

Translated by Wendy Doniger O'Flaherty
with Brian K Smith

No understanding of modern India is possible without this extraordinary model of jurisprudence, philosophy and religion, written from 200 BC to AD 200.

445404 448pp £9.99

NEW SONGS FROM A JADE TERRACE

An Anthology of Early Chinese Love Poetry

Translated by Anne Birrell with a foreword by Burton Watson and a critical essay by J H Prynne

A highly praised translation of an anthology of Chinese love poems compiled in approximately AD 545, which traces the development of the genre from the second century BC to its full flowering in the fifth and sixth centuries AD.

446508 448pp £8.99

POEMS OF HEAVEN AND HELL FROM ANCIENT MESOPOTAMIA

Translated with an introduction by N K Sandars

Five poems from the height of Babylonian civilization reflect the cyclical nature of the lives and beliefs of the Mesopotamian culture. Included are *The Babylonian Creation*, *The Sumerian Underworld*, *Inanna's Journey to Hell*, *Adapa: The Man*, and *A Prayer to the Gods of Night.*

442499 192pp £7.99

POEMS OF THE LATE T'ANG

Translated with an introduction by A C Graham

This volume introduces seven poets – Tu Fu, Meng Chiao, Han Yü, Lu T'ung, Li Ho, Tu Mu and Li Shang-yin – who flourished during the eighth and ninth centuries, the latter part of the golden age of Chinese literature.

441573 176pp £7.99

POEMS FROM THE SANSKRIT

Translated with an introduction by John Brough

Written between the fourth and tenth centuries AD, these secular poems illustrate the great diversity of subject matter, style and imagination in classical Sanskrit literature.

441980 160pp £6.25

THE RIG VEDA

Edited and translated by Wendy Doniger O'Flaherty

This collection of more than 1000 Sanskrit hymns from the timeless world of myth and ritual offers a unique insight into early Indian mythology, philosophy and religion.

444025 352pp £8.99

SIX YUAN PLAYS

Translated with an introduction by Liu Jung-En

Six vibrant plays from the thirteenth century represent the first real Chinese theatre to develop free from conservative Confucianism: *The Orphan of Chao, The Soul of Ch'ien-Nü Leaves Her Body, The Injustice Done to Tou Ngo, Chang Boils the Sea, Autumn in Han Palace* and *A Stratagem of Interlocking Rings.*

442626 288pp £9.99

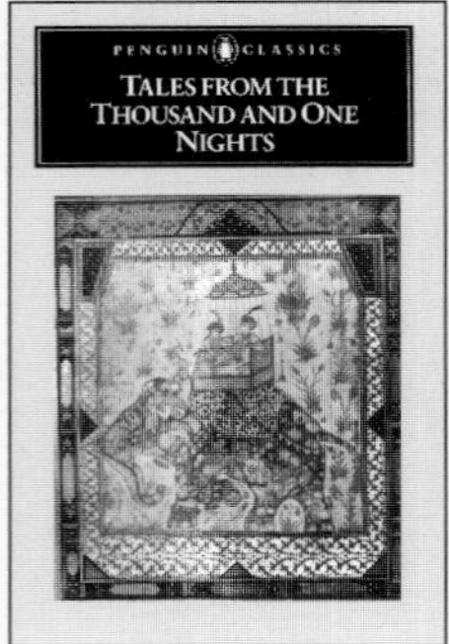

SPEAKING OF SIVA

Translated with an introduction by
A K Ramanujan

This volume contains a collection of *vacanas* (free-verse lyrics) centering on the Hindu god Shiva, written by four saints of the great bhakti protest movement of the tenth century AD: Basvanna, Devara, Dasimayya, Mahaadeviyakka and Allama Prabhu.

442707 208pp £7.99

TALES FROM THE THOUSAND AND ONE NIGHTS

Translated with an introduction by
N J Dawood

This volume includes the finest and best known of the *Tales*, representing an expression of the secular imagination in revolt against the religious austerity of other works of medieval Near Eastern literature.

442898 416pp £7.99

THE UPANISHADS

Translated with an introduction by
Juan Mascaro

First written in Sanskrit between 800 and 400 BC, these spiritual treatises form the foundation of Hindu beliefs.

441638 144pp £6.99

GREEK LITERATURE

Courtesy of Scala

AESCHYLUS

525-456 BC

The Oresteia

Agememnon/The Libation Bearers/ The Eumenides

Translated with an introduction by Robert Fagles, glossary by Robert Fagles and W B Stanford

The Oresteia - the only trilogy in Greek drama that survives from antiquity - takes on new depth and power in Fagle's acclaimed modern translation.

443339 336pp £6.99

The Oresteian Trilogy

Agamemnon/The Choephori/The Eumenides

Translated with an introduction by Philip Vellacott

Justice, vengeance, and the forces of fate provide the themes for *Agamemnon, The Choephori* and *The Eumenides.* Vellacott's verse translation is presented with a short introduction to Greek mythology and the historical context of the trilogy.

440674 208pp £5.99

Prometheus Bound and Other Plays

The Suppliants/Seven Against Thebes/ The Persians

Translated with an introduction by Philip Vellacott

Prometheus Bound, The Suppliants, Seven Against Thebes and *The Persians,* presented here in verse translation, demonstrate that reason, not violence, is the proper principle of civilized life.

441123 160pp £6.99

AESOP

c. 500 BC

The Complete Fables

Translated by Olivia and Robert Temple, with an introduction by Robert Temple

'This gem is the first *ever* publication in English of the complete fables. Written in the 6th century BC, they have long suffered from textual corruption and doubts about authorship. Everyone knows the classics, like the hare and the tortoise, but much of Aesop's work remains shadowy. In this brilliant work of restoration we can finally see the man whole: a deft and often sardonic miniaturist, capable of much more than twee stories about animals, and not the prissy moralist of expurgated children's editions.' *Daily Telegraph*

446494 288pp £5.99

APOLLONIUS OF RHODES

c. 200 BC

The Voyage of the Argo

Translated with an introduction by E V Rieu

Apollonius used the manner and matter of epics but wrote from a personal viewpoint, as a critical observer, in his *Argonautica*, the fullest surviving account of Jason's voyage in quest of the Golden Fleece.

440852 224pp £7.99

ARISTOPHANES

c. 448–380 BC

Birds/Wealth/Knights/Peace/ The Assembly Women

Translated with an introductions by David Barrett and Alan Sommerstein

Representing Aristophanes' sharply satirical comedy, this collection of plays is prefaced by an introduction to the history and literary style of the author.

443320 336pp £7.99

LYSISTRATA/THE ACHARNIANS/THE CLOUDS

Translated with an introduction by
Alan Sommerstein

Writing at a time when Athens was undergoing a crisis in its social attitudes, Aristophanes was an eloquent opponent of the demagogue and the sophist, and his comedy reveals a deep sympathy and longing for the return of a peaceful and honest way of life.

442871 256pp £7.99

WASPS/THE POET AND THE WOMEN/ THE FROGS

Translated with an introduction by
David Barrett

In this collection Aristophanes uses parody and low comedy to convey the spirit of Athens during the long, tragic war against Sparta.

441522 224pp £6.99

ARISTOTLE

384–322 BC

THE ART OF RHETORIC

Translated with an introduction by
Hugh Lawson-Tancred

With this book, Aristotle established the methods of informal reasoning, providing the first aesthetic evaluation of prose style and detailed observations of character and emotions.

445102 304pp £8.99

THE ATHENIAN CONSTITUTION

Translated with an introduction by
P J Rhodes

This is the single most important extant source for the study of the institutions of classical Athens. 'Clearly and accurately translated ... Lucid introduction and notes, and excellent analytical summaries, introduce each chapter.' S M Burstein, California State University

444319 208pp £6.99

DE ANIMA *(On the Soul)*

Translated with an introduction by
Hugh Lawson-Tancred

Considering the nature of life, Aristotle surveys and rejects the ideas of Plato and the pre-Socratics, developing his philosophy of the soul and mind, and introducing the central concepts of form and matter to explain perception, thought and motivation.

444718 256pp £7.99

THE ETHICS

The Nicomachean Ethics

Translated by J A K Thomson
Revised with appendices by Hugh Tredennick

Introduction and bibliography by
Jonathan Barnes

In a work that had tremendous impact on Western moral philosophy, Aristotle treats ethics as a practical rather than a theoretical science, and introduces psychology into the study of human behaviour.

440550 384pp £6.99

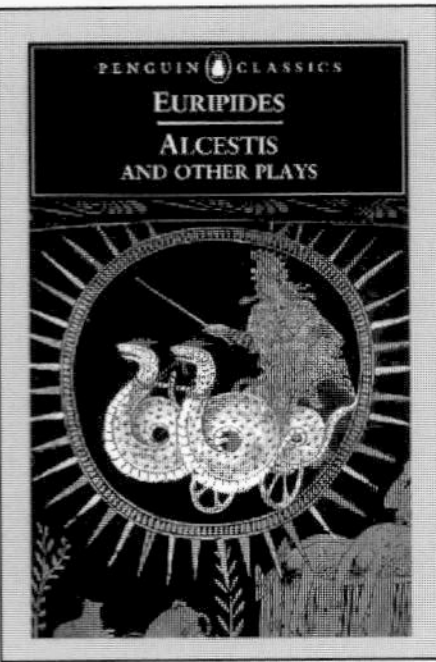

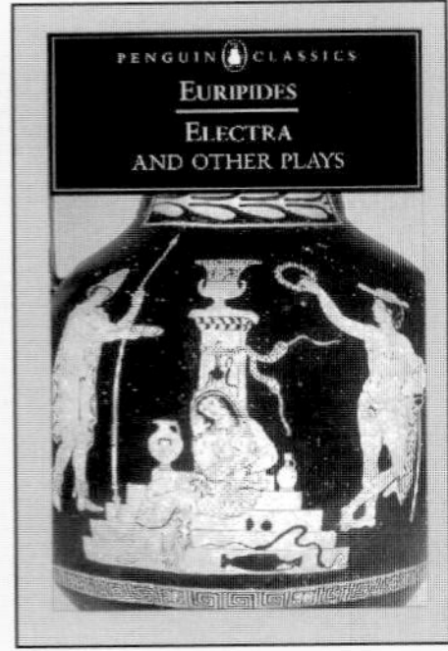

THE METAPHYSICS

Translated with an introduction by
Hugh Lawson-Tancred

In *The Metaphysics*, Aristotle laid the foundations for one of the central branches of Western philosophy integrating the natural and rational aspects of the world. In so doing he probed some of the deepest questions of philosophy.

446192 528pp £8.99

NEW OCTOBER 98

POETICS

Translated with an introduction by
Malcolm Heath

In one of the most perceptive and influential works of criticism in Western literary history, Aristotle examines the literature of his time, describing the origins of poetry as an imitative art and drawing attention to the distinctions between comedy and tragedy.

446362 144pp £6.99

THE POLITICS

Translated with an introduction by
T A Sinclair. Revised by Trevor J Saunders

The search for the ideal state and the best possible constitution is the basis for the last great work of Greek political thought.

444211 512pp £7.99

EURIPIDES

480–406 BC

ALCESTIS/IPHIGENIA IN TAURIS/HIPPOLYTUS

Translated with an introduction by
Philip Vellacott

Euripides acts as the sceptical questioner of his age in these verse translations.

440313 192pp £5.99

ALCESTIS AND OTHER PLAYS

Alcestis/Medea/The Children of Heracles/ Hippolytus

Translated by John Davie with an
introduction by Richard Rutherford

John Davie's new translation into dignified English prose makes one of the greatest Greek writers accessible once again to a wide public. Euripides was the key figure in transforming the familiar figures of Greek mythology from awe-inspiring but remote heroes into recognisable, fallible human beings.

446435 240pp £6.99

THE BACCHAE AND OTHER PLAYS

The Bacchae/Ion/The Women of Troy/Helen

Translated with an introduction by
Philip Vellacott

Four plays – *Ion* and *Helen* in prose and *The Bacchae* and *The Women of Troy* with dialogue rewritten in verse – depict the guilt and suffering of war, and the subsequent loss of faith.

440445 256pp £7.99

ELECTRA AND OTHER PLAYS

Andromache/Electra/Hecabe/Suppliant Women/ Trojan Women

Translated by John Davie, with introductions
by Richard Rutherford

'Euripides', wrote Aristotle, 'is the most intensely tragic of all the poets.' These plays reveal his questioning attitude to traditional

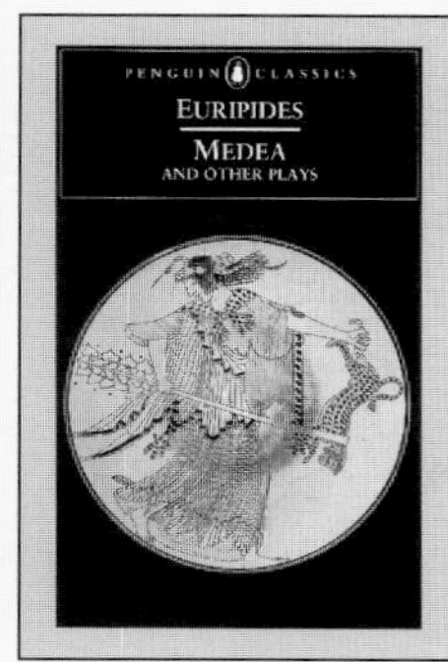

pieties, disconcerting shifts of sympathy, disturbingly eloquent evil characters and his acute insight into destructive passion, he is the most strikingly modern of ancient authors.
446680 304pp £6.99

MEDEA AND OTHER PLAYS

Medea/Hecabe/Electra/Heracles

Translated with an introduction by
Philip Vellacott

Euripides was the first playwright to use the chorus as commentator, to put contemporary language into the mouths of heroes, and to interpret human suffering withour reference to the gods. These verse translations capture all the brilliance of his work.
441298 208pp £6.99

ORESTES AND OTHER PLAYS

Orestes/The Children of Heracles/ Andromache/The Suppliant Women/ The Phoenician Women/Iphigenia in Aulis

Translated with an introduction by
Philip Vellacott

These six plays span the last twenty-five years of Euripides' life and the period of Athens' long and fatal war with Sparta, culminating in the fall of the city in 404 BC.
442596 448pp £8.99

HERODOTUS

c. 480–425 BC

THE HISTORIES

Translated by Aubrey de Selincourt and
revised with an introduction by
John M Marincola

Written during a period of increasing conflict between Sparta and Athens, these compelling descriptions of great battles, rulers, and political upheavals attempt to recapture the glorious past of a unified Greece.
446389 688pp £7.99

HESIOD AND THEOGNIS

c. 700 BC

THEOGONY/WORKS AND DAYS/ELEGIES

Translated with an introduction by
Dorothea Wender

Together these two poets – Hesiod, the epic poet, and Theognis, the elegist – offer a superb introduction to the life and thought of ancient Greece.
442839 176pp £6.99

HIPPOCRATES

c. 460–357 BC

HIPPOCRATIC WRITINGS

Edited by G E R Lloyd and translated by
J Chadwick, W N Mann, I M Lonie and
E T Withington

It is impossible to be certain which, if any, of these works were written by Hippocrates himself – his fame was such that many Greek medical writings became attributed to him. However they all share a concern with meticulous observation and an insistence on physical, not supernatural, causation of illness, revealing the origins not just of Western medicine but of scientific method.
444513 384pp £9.99

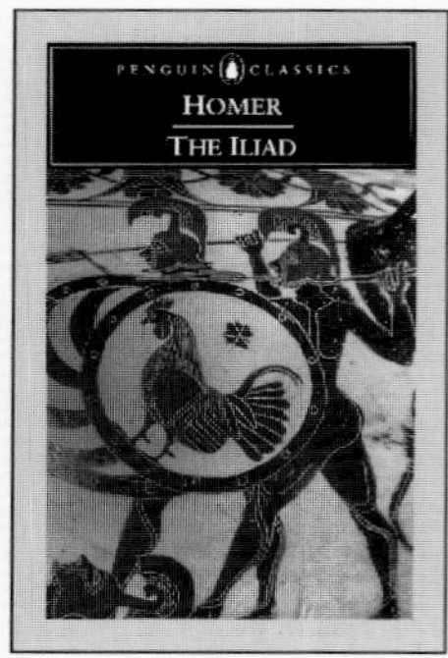

HOMER

c. 700 BC

THE ILIAD

Translated by Robert Fagles with
an introduction by Bernard Knox

Fagles combines his talents as poet and scholar to present this masterful, elegant translation of the stirring story of the Trojan War and the rage of Achilles.

445927 704pp £6.99

THE ILIAD

Prose translation with an introduction by
Martin Hammond

This prose translation captures the emotional power and the dramatic tension of the first and greatest literary achievement of Greek civilization.

444440 528pp £2.50

THE ILIAD

Translated by Alexander Pope
Edited with an introduction by
Steven Shankman

A classic of English translation, Pope's version of Homer's *Iliad* – 'certainly the noblest version of poetry,' in Dr Johnson's words, 'which the world has ever seen.'

445048 1248pp £15.99

THE ILIAD

Translated by E V Rieu

Rieu's original prose translation of *The Iliad* is a long-established classic.

440143 480pp £5.99

THE ODYSSEY

Translated by Robert Fagles
Introduction and notes by Bernard Knox

'Robert Fagles is the best living translator of ancient Greek drama, lyric poetry, and epic into modern English, and his translation of the *Odyssey* is his finest work so far.' *New Yorker*

268863 560pp £12.99

THE ODYSSEY

Translated by E V Rieu, revised by Dominic
Rieu with an introduction by Peter Jones

Odysseus's perilous ten-year voyage from Troy to his home in Ithaca is recounted in a revised translation that captures the swiftness, drama, and worldview of the Greek original.

445560 448pp £2.50

HOMER IN ENGLISH

Edited with an introduction by
George Steiner

From Chaucer's *Troilus and Criseyde* and Pound's *Cantos* to Joyce's *Ulysses* and Walcott's *Omeros*, Homer has been the most translated author in Western literature. This superb selection assembles the best translations from six and a half centuries.

446214 400pp £9.99

LONGUS

c. 200 BC

DAPHNIS AND CHLOE

Translated with an introduction by
Paul Turner

At the heart of much romantic literature of the modern era, this physically explicit and

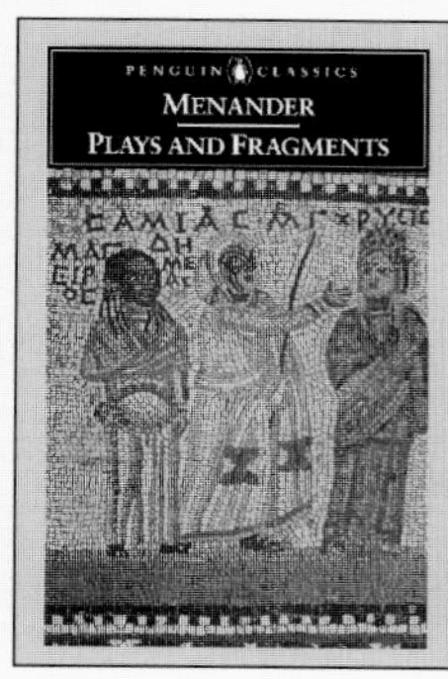

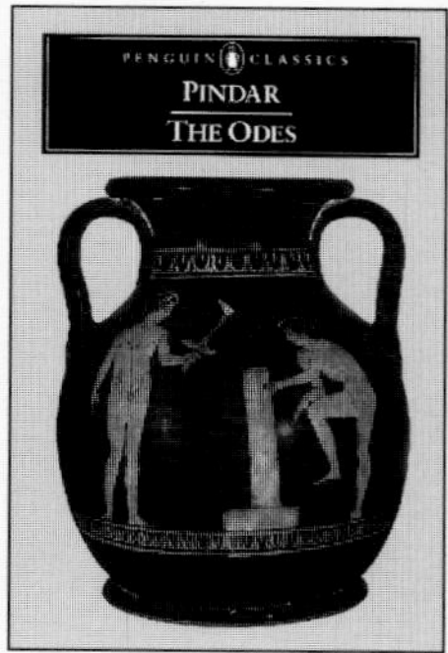

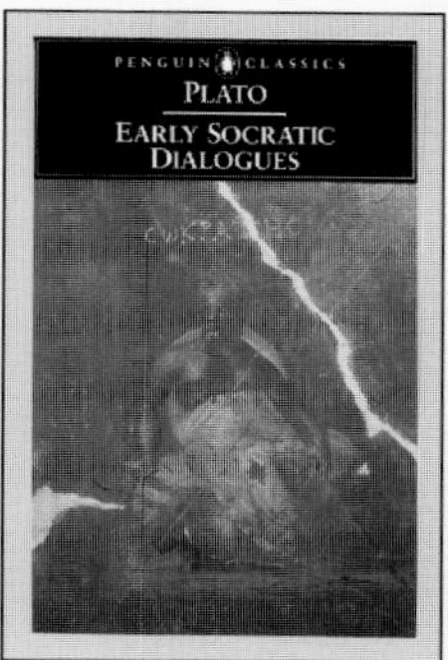

emotionally charged early novel holds an important place in the classical/European canon.
440593 128pp £6.99

MENANDER
342–292 BC

Plays and Fragments
Translated with an introduction by
Norma P Miller

The most innovative dramatist of the Greek New Comedy period, Menander concentrated on his characters' daily lives and colloquial speech in these comedies of manners. This selection contains all but two of Menander's surviving plays, passages attributed to him, and textual notes.
445013 272pp £8.99

PAUSANIAS
c. 150

Guide to Greece
Translated by Peter Levi

Pausanias's classic account of every Greek city and sanctuary includes historical introductions and a record of local customs and beliefs. Volume 1 covers central Greece, the country around Athens, Delphi, and Mycenae; Volume 2 describes southern Greece, including Olympia, Sparta, Arcadia, and Bassae.

Volume 1: Central
442251 608pp £9.99

Volume 2: Southern
44226X 560pp £10.99

PINDAR
522–443 BC

The Odes
Translated with an introduction by
C M Bowra

The entire spectrum of Greek moral order, from earthly competition to fate and mythology, is covered in Pindar's *Epinicia* – choral songs extolling victories in the games at Olympia, Delphi, Nemea, and Corinth.
44209X 256pp £7.99

PLATO
c. 428–348 BC

Early Socratic Dialogues
Edited with a general introduction by
Trevor J Saunders
Translated with introductions by
Trevor J Saunders, Iain Lane, Donald Watt
and Robin Waterfield

Rich in drama and humour, seven dialogues provide a definitive portrait of Socrates' thought and times. The selection includes *Ion*, *Laches*, *Lysis*, *Charmides*, *Hippias Major*, *Hippias Minor*, and *Euthydemus*.
444475 400pp £8.99

Gorgias
Translated with an introduction by
Walter Hamilton

Though Gorgias was a teacher of oratory, this dialogue is more concerned with ethics than with the art of public speaking.
440941 160pp £5.99

The Last Days of Socrates

Euthyphro/The Apology/Crito/Phaedro

Translated by Hugh Tredennick and Harold Tarrant with an introduction by Harold Tarrant

The four superb Platonic dialogues that form the classic account of the trial and death of Socrates have almost as central a place in Western consciousness as the trial and death of Jesus.

44582X 272pp £6.99

The Laws

Translated with an introduction by Trevor J Saunders

In his last and longest work, Plato sets forth a detailed code of immutable laws for the ideal state that contrasts sharply with the notion of the philosopher-king developed in *The Republic*.

442227 560pp £8.99

Phaedrus and Letters VII and VIII

Translated with an introduction by Walter Hamilton

Phaedrus, chiefly valued for its idyllic setting and magnificent myth, is concerned with establishing the principles of rhetoric based on the knowledge of truth inspired by love. The seventh and eighth letters reflect Plato's involvement in Sicilian politics and reveal fascinating glimpses into the contemporary power struggle.

442758 160pp £6.99

Philebus

Translated with an introduction by Robin Waterfield

This is Plato's most deliberate and thorough attempt to describe the good life and the way people ought to achieve it, presented with an extensive critical introduction covering the main stages of the dialogue.

443959 160pp £6.99

Protagoras and Meno

Translated with an introduction by W K C Guthrie

These two dialogues explore the question of virtue, the first concluding that all virtues are united by knowledge, the second arguing that virtue is teachable.

440682 160pp £5.99

The Republic

Translated with an introduction by Desmond Lee

The first great piece of utopian writing, Plato's treatise on an ideal state applies philosophical principles to political affairs.

440488 448pp £2.50

The Symposium

Revised translation with an introduction by Christopher Gill

Among the most powerful and moving of Plato's dialogues, the *Symposium* is perhaps the greatest of all literary works exploring the nature of love in Western thought. Full of drama, humour and sharply drawn characters, it offers profound insights into gender roles, sex in society and the value of sublimating our basic instincts.

446168 144pp £5.99

NEW MARCH 99

The Symposium

Translated with an introduction by Walter Hamilton

440240 128pp £4.99

Theaetetus

Translated with an introduction by Robin Waterfield

Plato examines the idea of knowledge, putting forth and criticizing opposing definitions in this pioneering work in epistemology.

444505 256pp £7.99

Timaeus and Critias

Translated with an introduction by Desmond Lee

The earliest Greek account of a divine creation, *Timaeus* is concerned with cosmology and anthropology. The unfinished *Critias*, Plato's only work on the natural sciences, tells the story of the lost civilization of Atlantis.

442618 176pp £6.99

PLOTINUS

c. 203–262

The Enneads

Translated by Stephen MacKenna and abridged with an introduction by John Dillon

Here is a highly original synthesis of Platonism, mystic passion, ideas from Greek philosophy, and variants of the Trinity and other central tenets of Christian doctrine by the brilliant thinker who has had an immense influence on mystics and religious writers.

44520X 688pp £10.99

PLUTARCH

c. 50–125

The Age of Alexander

Translated and annotated by Ian Scott-Kilvert with an introduction by G T Griffith

Taken from *The Parallel Lives*, this history of nine great Greek statesmen – Agesilaus, Pelopidas, Dion, Timoleon, Demosthenes, Phocion, Alexander, Demetrius, and Pyrrhus – traces a crucial phase of ancient history, from the fall of Athens to the rise of Macedonia.

442863 448pp £8.99

Essays

Edited with an introduction by Ian Kidd
Translated by Robin Waterfield

Whether he is offering abstract speculations or practical ethics, reflections on the benefits of military versus intellectual glory, or the reasoning powers of animals, Plutarch's encyclopedic writings form a treasure trove of ancient wisdom.

445641 448pp £9.99

The Fall of the Roman Republic

Translated by Rex Warner
with introductions by Robin Seager

Selections on Gaius, Marius, Sulla, Crasus, Pompey, Caesar and Cicero are taken from *The Parallel Lives*. Plutarch records, simply and dramatically, the long and bloody period of foreign and civil war that marked the collapse of the Roman Republic and ushered in the Empire.

440844 368pp £8.99

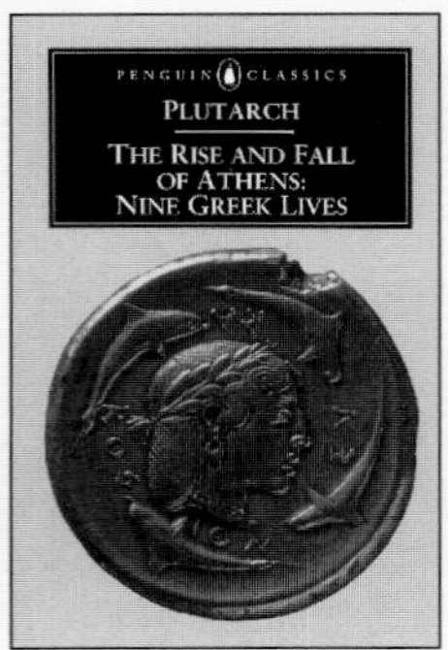

THE MAKERS OF ROME

Translated with an introduction by
Ian Scott-Kilvert

Nine of Plutarch's *Roman Lives* - Coriolanus, Fabius Maximus, Marcellus, Cato the Elder, Tiberius Gracchus, Gaius Gracchus, Sertorius, Brutus and Mark Anthony - illustrate the courage and tenacity of the Romans in war and their genius for political compromise, from the earliest years of the Republic to the establishment of the Empire.

441581 368pp £8.99

PLUTARCH ON SPARTA

Translated with introduction by
Richard J A Talbert

Rich in anecdote and personal idiosyncrasy, Plutarch's writings are a literary, philosophical, and social exploration of this extraordinary Greek city.

444637 224pp £7.99

THE RISE AND FALL OF ATHENS

Translated with an introduction by
Ian Scott-Kilvert

Nine Greek biographies illustrate the rise and fall of Athens, from the legendary days of Theseus, the city's founder, through Solon, Themistocles, Aristides, Cimon, Pericles, Nicias, and Alcibiades, to the razing of its walls by Lysander.

441026 320pp £7.99

SOPHOCLES

496–406 BC

ELECTRA AND OTHER PLAYS

Ajax/Electra/Women of Trachis/Philoctetes

Translated with an introduction by
E F Watling

These verse translations exhibit the structure that set the standard for most modern dramatic works.

440283 224pp £5.99

THREE THEBAN PLAYS

Antigone/Oedipus the King/Oedipus at Colonus

Translated by Robert Fagles with an
introduction by Bernard Knox

Fagle's lucid modern translation captures the majesty of Sophocles's master-work, and is enhanced by introductions to each play, an essay on the history of the text, extensive notes, bibliography, and glossary.

444254 432pp £5.99

THE THEBAN PLAYS

King Oedipus/Oedipus at Colonus/Antigone

Translated with an introduction by
E F Watling

Based on the legend of the royal house of Thebes, *King Oedipus*, *Oedipus at Colonus*, and *Antigone* are Sophocles' tragic masterpieces. This verse translation is supplemented by E F Watling's introduction, which places Sophocles in historical context, discusses the origins of the art of drama, and interprets each play in the Theban legend.

440038 176pp £2.50

THEOCRITUS

c. 308–240 BC

THE IDYLLS

Translated with an introduction by Robert Wells

From Sicilian legend to the sexual gossip of herdsmen, these second-century BC pastorals are presented in modern-verse translations that reveal Theocritus as a varied and compelling poet.

445234 160pp £6.99

THUCYDIDES

c. 460–395 BC

HISTORY OF THE PELOPONNESIAN WAR

Translated by Rex Warner with an introduction by M I Finley

The eight books of Thucydides' account of the clash between two great powers, Athens and Sparta, are contained in Rex Warner's acclaimed modern translation.

440399 656pp £8.99

XENOPHON

c. 430–352 BC

CONVERSATIONS OF SOCRATES

Translated by Hugh Tredennick and Robin Waterfield, edited with new material by Robin Waterfield

Xenophon's complete Socratic works – *Socrates' Defence*, *Memoirs of Socrates*, *The Dinner Party* and *The Estate-Manager* – not only portray the character and teachings of the great philosopher but apply Socratic principles to the daily life of Greece, giving insight into the religious, political, and moral views of the Athenians.

44517X 384pp £7.99

HIERO THE TYRANT AND OTHER TREATISES

Translated by Robin Waterfield
Introductions by Paul Cartledge

An Athenian aristocrat who fought as a mercenary commander in Cyrus the Younger's campaign to seize the Persian throne in 401 BC, Xenophon wrote a gripping account of that expedition as well as many other works of history, politics and philosophy. The six works collected here offer his informed insights into the nature and purposes of leadership.

446826 288pp £7.99

A HISTORY OF MY TIMES

Translated by Rex Warner with an introduction by George Cawkwell

Continuing the story of the Peloponnesian War where Thucydides left off, Xenophon records the politics and battles that brought about the ultimate decline of Greece.

441751 432pp £8.99

THE PERSIAN EXPEDITION

Translated by Rex Warner with an introduction by George Cawkwell

This historical account tells of Xenophon's march with the Ten Thousand against the barbarian Persians.

440070 384pp £7.99

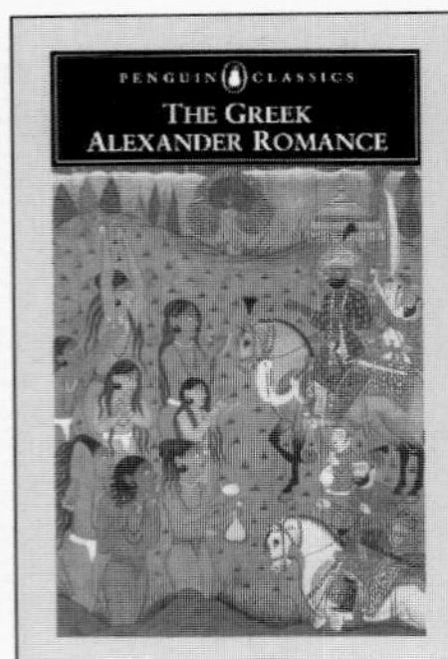

ANTHOLOGIES

CLASSICAL LITERARY CRITICISM

Translated with an introduction by
T S Dorsch

This collection presents three classical discussions of creative writing: Aristotle's *Poetics*, Horace's *Ars Poetica*, and the treatise *On The Sublime*, falsely attributed to Dionysius Longinus.

441557 160pp £6.99

EARLY GREEK PHILOSOPHY

Translated and edited with an introduction by Jonathan Barnes

The earliest Western philosophers, the pre-Socratics, are profiled in this omnibus, which includes a general introduction and a synopsis of their historical and ideological development, as well as brief introductions to each philosopher's work.

444610 320pp £8.99

THE GREEK ALEXANDER ROMANCE

Translated with an introduction by
Richard Stoneman

One of the most influential works of late classical Greek literature, this fast-paced, wonderfully exuberant entertainment portrays the fabulous adventures of Alexander the Great.

445609 208pp £8.99

THE GREEK ANTHOLOGY

A Selection in Modern Verse Translation

Edited by Peter Jay

Arranged chronologically from the seventh century BC to the sixth century AD, 850 epitaphs, satires, jokes, pastoral epigrams and poems of love and friendship have been translated by distinguished American and British poets.

442855 448pp £10.99

GREEK LITERATURE

An Anthology

Edited and selected with an introduction by
Michael Grant

The whole range of Greek poetry and prose is highlighted, from Homer and Hesiod to the Hellenistic poets and the work of Ptolemy, Galen and Plotinus.

443231 496pp £9.99

GREEK POLITICAL ORATORY

Edited, selected and translated with an introduction by A N W Saunders

These fifteen representative orations made by Thucydides, Lysias, Andocides, Isocrates, and Demosthenes highlight the Greek mastery of public rhetoric and persuasion that marked the years between 510 and 336 BC.

442235 272pp £7.99

LATIN AND ROMAN LITERATURE

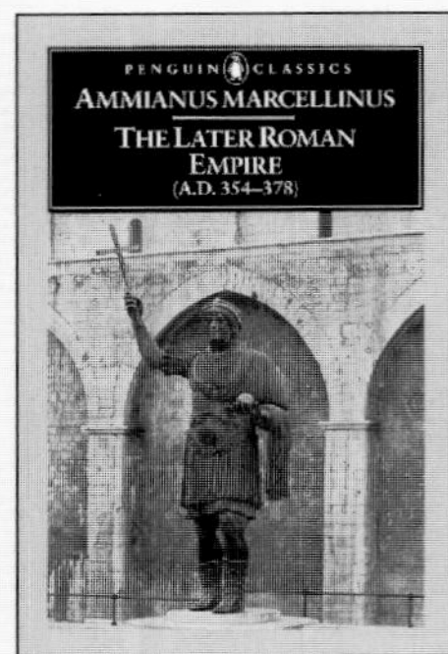

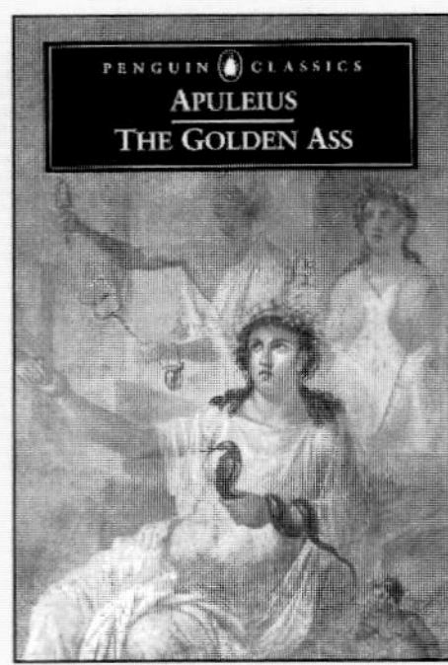

AMMIANUS MARCELLINUS

c. 330

The Later Roman Empire

AD 354–378

Selected and translated by
William R Hamilton with an introduction by
Andrew Wallace-Hadrill

Considered to be the last great Roman historian, Ammianus Marcellinus continues the histories of Tacitus, describing the reigns of the emperors Constantius, Julian, Jovian, Valentinian and Valens.

444068 512pp £9.99

APPIAN

c. 2nd century AD

The Civil Wars

Translated with an introduction by
John Carter

Covering the period from 133 to 35 BC, this exploration of the decline of the Roman state details the struggles of Marius against Sulla, Caesar against Pompeius, and Antonius and Octavian against Caesar's assassins, Brutus and Cassius.

445099 480pp £8.99

APULEIUS

c. 125–170

The Golden Ass

Translated with an introduction by
E. J. Kenney

Written in the racy, extravagant style of the professional story-tellers of the time, *The Golden Ass* is nevertheless a moral work. It recounts the boisterous, often bawdy, adventures of a young man who has the misfortune to be turned into an ass, falls into the hands of robbers, shares their fantastic exploits and is finally turned back into a man by the goddess Isis.

435905 320pp £6.99

ARRIAN

c. 90–145

The Campaigns of Alexander

Translated by Aubrey de Selincourt,
revised with an introduction by J R Hamilton

Written four hundred years after Alexander's death, this is the most reliable account of the conqueror's life, character and achievements.

442537 432pp £8.99

MARCUS AURELIUS

121–180

Meditations

Translated with an introduction by
Maxwell Staniforth

It was during his campaigns against the barbarians that the Roman Emperor, Marcus Aurelius (AD 121–180), wrote his famous *Meditations*. They record the passing thoughts, the maxims, the musings on life an death of a sensitive and humble mind which had been trained in the Stoic philosophy that contributed so much to Christianity.

441409 192pp £5.99

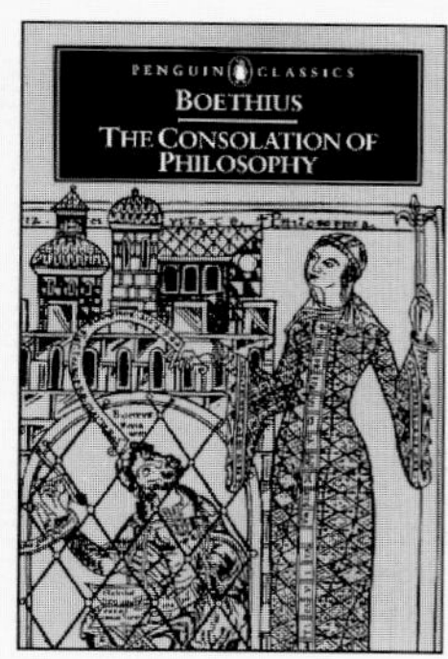

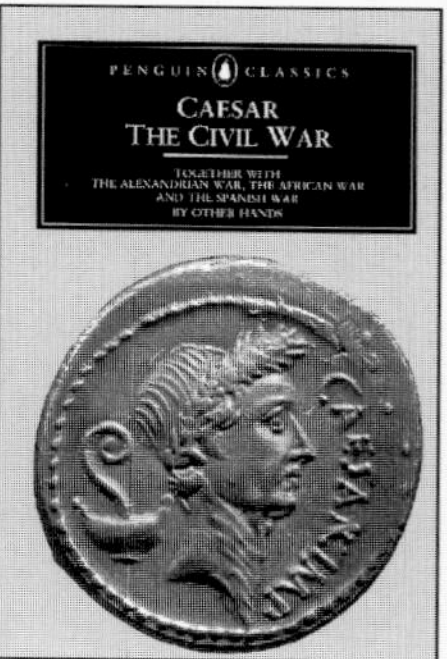

ANCIUS BOETHIUS

475–525

The Consolation of Philosophy

Translated with an introduction by V E Watts

This influential book mingles verse and prose in a sacred dialogue reflecting the doctrines of Plato, Aristotle, the Stoics and the Neoplatonists.

442081 192pp £7.99

JULIUS CAESAR

c. 100–44 BC

The Civil War

Translated with an introduction by Jane F Gardner

A general of genius, Caesar was also a vivid and powerful writer. These accounts paint a full and surprisingly fair picture of the great struggle that brought Caesar to power and then caused his death.

441875 368pp £7.99

The Conquest of Gaul

Translated by S A Handford and revised with an introduction by Jane F Gardner

Caesar's account of the Gallic Wars, although based on fact, also served to impress his contemporaries and justify himself to his enemies. The earliest eyewitness account of Britain and its inhabitants appears in these famous memoirs.

444335 272pp £6.99

CATULLUS

c. 84–54 BC

The Poems of Catullus

Translated with an introduction by Peter Whigham

These 111 poems introduce the lyric poet Catullus, master of the pungent epigram, who found his inspiration in the glittering Roman society of the late Republic.

441808 256pp £6.99

MARCUS TULLIUS CICERO

106–43 BC

Murder Trials

Translated with an introduction by Michael Grant

Cicero was still in his twenties when he got Sextus Roscius off a charge of murdering his father and nearly sixty when he defended King Deiotarus, accused of trying to murder Caesar. In between he built a reputation as the greatest orator of his time. His clients generally went free. And in vindicating men – who sometimes did not deserve it – he left us a mass of detail about Roman life, law and history.

44288X 288pp £7.99

The Nature of the Gods

Translated by Horace C P McGregor with an introduction by J M Ross

In *De natura deorum*, Cicero sets out the ancient Greeks' conclusions about the existence and nature of deities and the extent of their involvement in human affairs.

442650 288pp £8.99

ON GOVERNMENT

Translated with an introduction by Michael Grant

These pioneering writings on the mechanics, tactics and strategies of government were devised by the Roman Republic's most enlightened thinker.

445951 432pp £8.99

ON THE GOOD LIFE

Translated with an introduction by Michael Grant

This collection of Cicero's writings discusses duty, friendship, the training of a statesman, and the importance of moral integrity in the search for happiness.

442448 384pp £7.99

SELECTED LETTERS

Translated with an introduction by D R Shackleton Bailey

This selection of thirteen letters chosen from Volumes 1 and 2 of Cicero's *Letters to His Friends* chronicles the political and social life of a dying civilization.

444580 288pp £8.99

SELECTED POLITICAL SPEECHES

Translated with an introduction by Michael Grant

The seven speeches in this volume, annotated to supply the relevant political history of the period, include the speeches against the Catiline conspiracy as well as the first 'Philippic' against Mark Antony.

442146 336pp £8.99

SELECTED WORKS

Translated with an introduction by Michael Grant

Divided into two parts – 'Against Tyranny' and 'How to Live' – this selection of Cicero's work reveals the private and public sides of his liberal personality and his opposition to oppressive and unparliamentary methods of government.

440992 272pp £8.99

CASSIUS DIO

163–235

THE ROMAN HISTORY

Translated by Ian Scott-Kilvert and with an introduction by John Carter

Following Rome's long road to peace after decades of civil war, Cassius Dio provides the fullest account of the reign of the first emperor in Books 50 through to 60 of his *Roman History*.

444483 368pp £9.99

HORACE

65–8 BC

THE COMPLETE ODES AND EPODES

Translated by W G Shepherd with an introduction by Betty Radice

The elusive personality and ironic philosophy of Horace are exemplified in seventeen epodes, 103 odes and *The Centennial Hymn.*

44422X 256pp £8.99

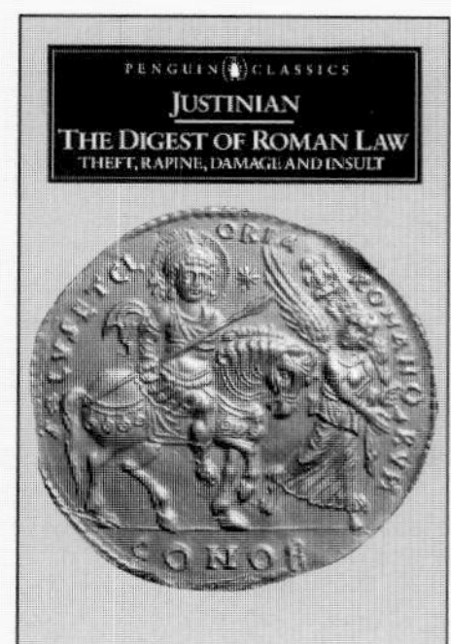

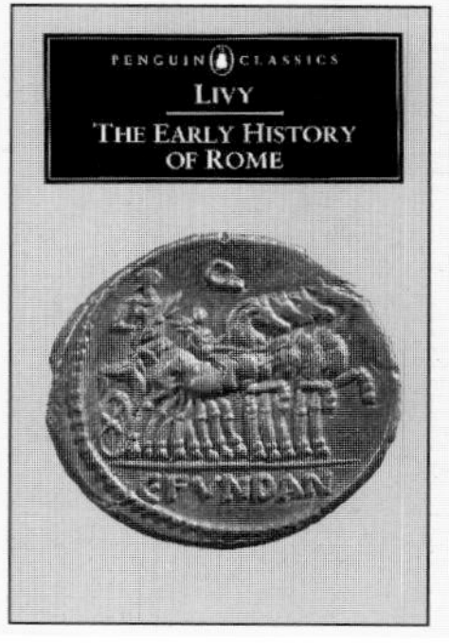

HORACE IN ENGLISH

Edited by D S Carne-Ross and Kenneth Hayes with an introduction by D S Carne-Ross

This anthology brings together a diverse group of Latin-to-English translations of Horace's *Odes*, *Epodes*, *Satires* and *Epistles*. It contains well-known translations, as well as ones that reflect the conventions and poetic style of the translator's own time or that offer fresh readings of Horace's centuries-old masterpieces.

423877 576pp £9.99

HORACE AND PERSIUS

65–8 BC AD 34–62

THE SATIRES

Translated and with an introduction by Niall Rudd

The broad range of the controversial Roman poetic form the satura is illustrated in eighteen satires and twenty-three epistles of Horace and six metaphorical essays of the Stoic critic Persius, presented in modern verse translation.

442790 304pp £8.99

FLAVIUS JOSEPHUS

c. 37–98

THE JEWISH WAR

Translated by G A Williamson, revised with an introduction by Mary Smallwood

Josephus depicts in vivid detail the Jewish rebellion of AD 66, supplying much of the available information on first century Palestine.

444203 512pp £9.99

JUSTINIAN

527–565

THE DIGEST OF ROMAN LAW

Translated with an introduction by Colin Kolbert

Codified by Justinian I and published under his aegis in AD 533, this celebrated work of legal history forms a fascinating picture of ordinary life in Rome.

443436 192pp £7.99

JUVENAL

c. 55–138

THE SIXTEEN SATIRES

Translated with an introduction by Peter Green

Juvenal's *Satires* create a fascinating world of whores, fortune-tellers, boozy politicians, slick lawyers, shameless sycophants, ageing flirts and downtrodden teachers. Perhaps more than any other writer, Juvenal captures the splendour, the squalor and the sheer vibrant energy of everyday Roman life.

447040 320pp £7.99

NEW AUGUST 98

LIVY

59 BC–AD 17

THE EARLY HISTORY OF ROME

Translated by Aubrey de Sélincourt with an introduction by R M Ogilvie

The first five books of Livy's monumental *History of Rome* trace the foundation of Rome through the Gallic invasion of the fourth century BC.

441042 432pp £8.99

Rome and Italy

Translated and annotated by Betty Radice with an introduction by R M Ogilvie

Books 6 to 10 cover a dramatic century – from Rome's apparent collapse after defeat by the Gauls in 386 BC to its emergence as the premier power in Italy in 293 BC.

443886 384pp £8.99

Rome and the Mediterranean

Translated by Henry Bettenson with an introduction by A H McDonald

Books 31 to 45 cover the years from 201 BC to 167 BC, when Rome emerged as ruler of the Mediterranean.

443185 704pp £9.99

The War with Hannibal

Edited with an introduction by Betty Radice Translated by Aubrey de Selincourt

Books 21 to 30 cover the declaration of the Second Punic War in 218 BC to the battle in 202 BC at Zama in Africa, where Hannibal was finally defeated.

44145X 712pp £9.99

LUCRETIUS

99–55 BC

On the Nature of the Universe

Translated with an introduction by R E Latham

Revised with an introduction by John Godwin

This edition of the classic poem and seminal test of Epicurean science and philosophy – which shaped human understanding of the world for centuries – brings new textual research and additional context to Lucretius's explorations of spirit, mind and soul.

446109 336pp £7.99

MARTIAL

40–104

The Epigrams

Selected and translated by James Michie with an introduction by Peter Howell

Scabrous, affectionate, cruel, playful, Martial's highly polished epigrams celebrate the modern megaloplis that was first-century Rome. Latin originals appear alongside English translations in this dual-language edition.

443509 208pp £6.99

OVID

43 BC–AD 17

The Erotic Poems

Translated with an introduction by Peter Green

These works by the foremost erotic poet of the Augustan period – *The Art of Love*, the *Amores*, *Cures for Love*, and *On Facial Treatment for Ladies* – give testament to the whole spectrum of sexual behaviour.

443606 464pp £9.99

Heroides

Translated by Harold Isbell

Dramatic monologues in the form of love letters written between mythological lovers – such as Paris and Helen, and Hero and Leander – demonstrate Ovid's gift for psychological insight.

423559 288pp £8.99

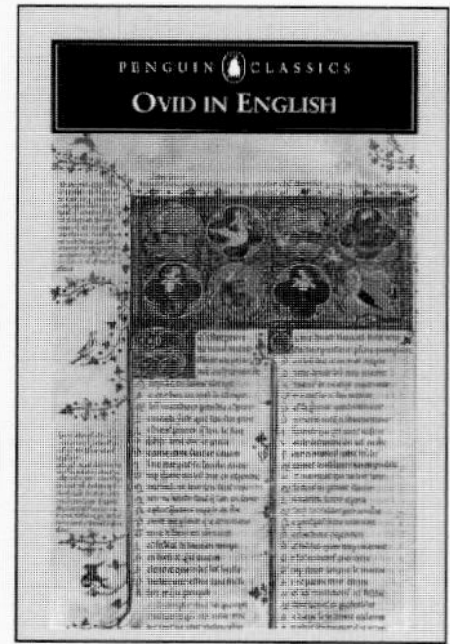

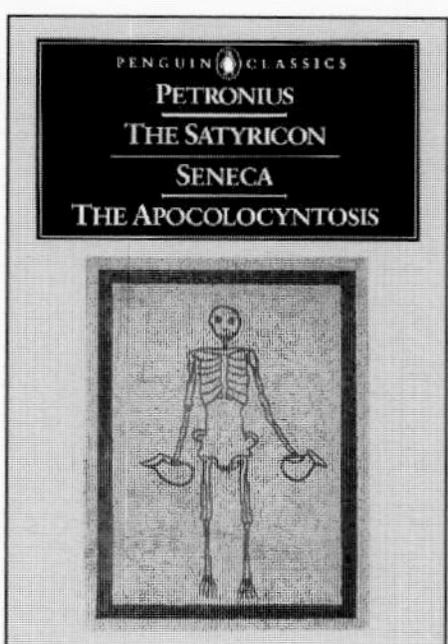

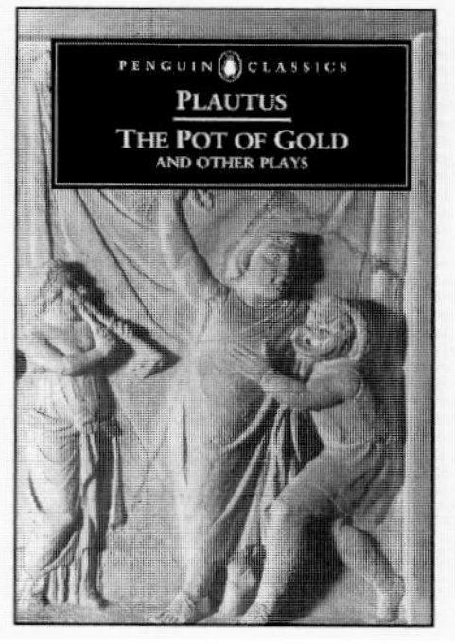

THE METAMORPHOSES

Translated with an introduction by
Mary M Innes

Culled from Greek poems and myths, Latin folklore, and tales from Babylon and the East, Ovid's *Metamorphoses* is examined in historical and literary context in Mary Innes's introduction.

440585 368pp £7.99

OVID IN ENGLISH

Edited with an introduction by Christopher Martin

Witty, erotic, sceptical and subversive, Ovid has been a seminal presence in English literature from the time of Chaucer and Caxton to Ted Hughes and Seamus Heaney. This superb collection brings together complete elegies from the *Amores*, *Heroides* and poems of exile, as well as many self-contained episodes from longer works, revealing both the sheer variety of Ovid's genius and the range of his impact on the British imagination.

446699 464pp £9.99
NEW JUNE 98

THE POEMS OF EXILE

Translated with an introduction and glossary by Peter Green

These poems, written during his exile from Rome on charges of literary obscenity, reveal Ovid's political opinions and his laments for his homeland.

444076 528pp £7.99

PETRONIUS AND SENECA

d. AD 66 c. 4 BC – AD 65

THE SATYRICON/APOCOLOCYNTOSIS

Translated with an introduction by
J P Sullivan

In *The Satyricon*, the racy adventures of the impotent Encolpius and his friends and lovers provide the definitive portrait of the age of Nero. *The Apocolcyntosis* is a malicious skit on the 'deification of Claudius the Clod', designed by Seneca to ingratiate himself with Claudius's sucessor, Nero.

444890 256pp £7.99

PLAUTUS

c. 254–184 BC

THE POT OF GOLD AND OTHER PLAYS

The Pot of Gold/The Prisoners/The Brothers Menaechmus/The Swaggering Soldier/Pseudolus

Translated by E F Watling

Plautus's broad humour, reflecting Roman manners and contemporary life, is revealed in these five plays.

441492 272pp £7.99

THE ROPE AND OTHER PLAYS

The Ghost/The Rope/A Three-Dollar Day/ Amphitryo

Translated with an introduction by
E F Watling

This translation presents the plays in a form suitable for the modern stage.

441360 288pp £7.99

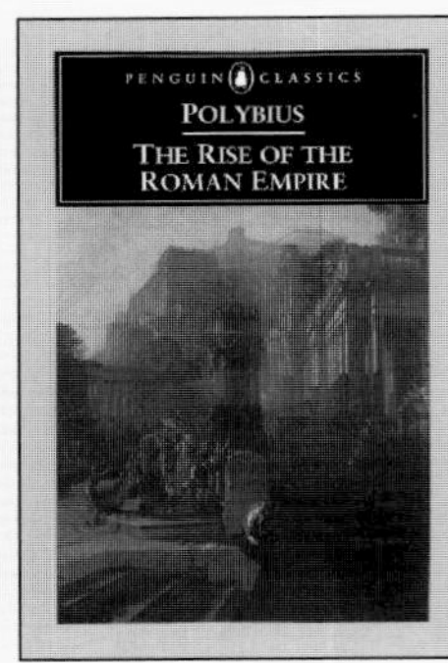

PLINY THE ELDER

23–79

NATURAL HISTORY: A SELECTION

Translated and with an introduction by John F Healy

This encyclopedic account of the state of science, art, and technology in the first century AD also provides a substantial volume of evidence about Pliny's character, temperament and attitude toward life. Including more than 20,000 facts – from agriculture, astronomy, botany, and chemistry to geography, pharmacy, and zoology – this work is the major source of ancient beliefs about every form of useful knowledge.

444130 448pp £9.99

PLINY THE YOUNGER

62–112

THE LETTERS OF THE YOUNGER PLINY

Translated and with an introduction by Betty Radice

This modern translation of the ten books of Pliny's *Letters* provides a wealth of information on the social and political history of Rome at the turn of the first century. Including Pliny's famous account of the destruction of Pompeii and his celebrated correspondence with the Emperor Trajan about the early Christians.

441271 320pp £7.99

POLYBIUS

c. 200–118 BC

THE RISE OF THE ROMAN EMPIRE

Translated by Ian Scott-Kilvert with an introduction by F W Walbank

The forty books of Polybius's *Universal History*, covering events in the third and second centuries BC that led to the supremacy of Rome, present the first panoramic view of history.

443622 576pp £9.99

PROCOPIUS

500–565

THE SECRET HISTORY

Translated with an introduction by G A Williamson

The other side of sixth-century Byzantium is revealed as Procopius exposes the vicious, scheming nature of the splendid empire and its rulers.

441824 208pp £7.99

PROPERTIUS

c. 50–16 BC

THE POEMS

Translated by W G Shepard and with an introduction by Betty Radice

These poems are written with a sensitivity to sound and imagery that transcend the limits of traditional Latin poetry and create an unforgettable picture of a brilliant but tormented man.

444645 224pp £6.99

QUINTUS CURTIUS RUFUS

d. 53

THE HISTORY OF ALEXANDER

Translated by John Yardley with
an introduction by Waldemar Heckel

Although no other human being has attracted so much speculation, Alexander himself remains an enigma. Curtius's *History* offers a great deal of information unavailable elsewhere. It also provides by far the most plausible and haunting portrait of Alexander we possess: a brilliantly realized image of a man ruined by constant good fortune in his youth.

444122 352pp £8.99

SALLUST

86–35

THE JUGURTHINE WAR
THE CONSPIRACY OF CATILINE

Translated and with an introduction
by S A Handford

These are the only surviving works by a man who held various public offices in Rome and was a friend of Caesar's and an opponent of Cicero's.

441328 240pp £7.99

SENECA

4 BC–AD 65

DIALOGUES AND LETTERS

Translated with an introduction by
C D N Costa

Included in this volume are the dialogues *On the Shortness of Life* and *On Tranquillity of Mind*, which are eloquent classic statements of Stoic ideals of fortitude and self-reliance. This selection also features extracts from *Natural Questions*, Seneca's exploration of such phenomena as the cataracts of the Nile and earthquakes, and the *Consolation of Helvia*, in which he tenderly tries to soothe his mother's pain at their separation.

446796 160pp £6.99

FOUR TRAGEDIES AND OCTAVIA

Translated with an introduction by
E F Watling

Although their themes are borrowed from Greek drama, these exuberant and often macabre plays focus on action rather than moral concerns and are strikingly different in style from Seneca's prose writing. This collection includes *Phaedra*, *Oedipus*, *Thyestes* and *The Trojan Women*.

441743 320pp £7.99

LETTERS FROM A STOIC

Selected and translated with an introduction
by Robin Campbell

Ranging from lively epistles to serious essays, these 124 letters selected from *Epistulae Morales* and *Lucilium* espouse the philosophy of Stoicism. This volume includes Tacitus's account of Seneca's death.

442103 256pp £7.99

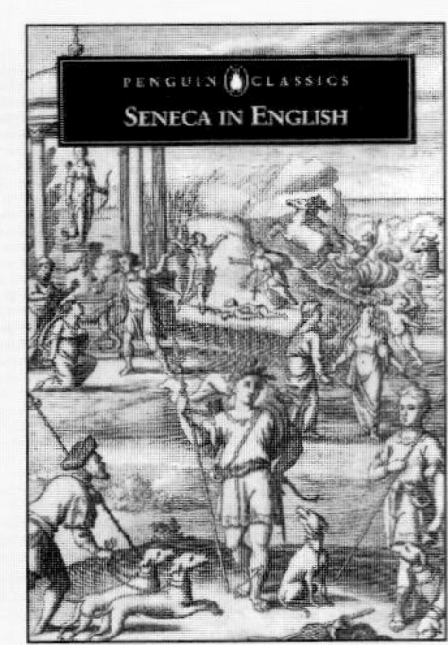

Seneca in English

Edited with an introduction by Don Share

Playwright and philosopher Seneca the Younger wrote in a violent, epigrammatic and extreme style. His works were imitated by writers ranging from Jonson to Johnson, from Milton to Marvel, and, in our own turbulent century, they have also inspired T S Eliot, Robert Lowell and Ted Hughes. This superb selection of translations, adaptations and variations vividly demonstrates Seneca's powerful continuing presence in English poetry.

446672 288pp £9.99

SUETONIUS

70–140

The Twelve Caesars

Translated by Robert Graves, revised with an introduction by Michael Grant

This fascinating and colourful Latin history vividly records incidents in the lives of the first twelve Caesars: Julius, Augustus, Tiberius, Gaius (Caligula), Claudius, Nero, Galba, Otho, Vitellius, Vespasian, Titus and Domitian.

440720 368pp £7.99

TACITUS

55–115

The Agricola/The Germania

Translated with an introduction by H Mattingley and revised by S A Handford

The Agricola, Tacitus's eulogistic description of his father-in-law, the governor of Roman Britain, contains the first detailed account of the British Isles. *The Germania*, an ethnographical account of the Germanic tribes, contrasts the primitive virtues of the Germans with the degeneracy of contemporary Rome.

442413 176pp £6.99

The Annals of Imperial Rome

Translated with an introduction by Michael Grant

Surviving passages form Tacitus's last and best-known work cover the reigns of Tiberius, Gaius (Caligula), Claudius, and Nero, and detail the Roman Empire at its zenith.

440607 464pp £8.99

The Histories

Translated with an introduction by Kenneth Wellesley

The surviving books of *The Histories* reconstruct the terrible events of the year of the Four Emperors (AD 69), which shook the whole edifice of the Empire.

441506 368pp £8.99

TERENCE

180–159 BC

The Comedies

The Girl from Andros/The Self-Tormentor/ The Eunuch/Phormio/The Mother-in-Law/ The Brothers

Translated with an introduction by Betty Radice

All six of the Roman dramatist's comedies – from *The Girl from Andros*, the first romantic comedy ever written, to the socially sophisticated *The Brothers* – show why Terence became a model for playwrights from the Renaissance onward.

44324X 400pp £8.99

VIRGIL

70–19 BC

The Aeneid

Translated by John Dryden

Edited by Frederick M Keener

Virgil's epic vividly recounts Aeneas's tortuous journey after the Trojan War and the struggles he faced as he laid the foundations for the greatest continental empire. Rendered into a vigorous and refined English by the most important man of letters of the seventeenth century, this translation of the *Aeneid* 'set a new, august standard so influential as to be epochal'. For his versions, John Dryden drew on the deep understanding of political unrest he had acquired during the civil wars of 1642–51 and the Glorious Revolution of 1688.

446273 480pp £9.99

The Aeneid

Translated with an introduction by David West

'It is the most truthful translation ever, conveying as many nuances and whispers as are possible from the original. This is a highly rhetorical version of an intensely rhetorical poem.' Philip Howard

444572 368pp £5.99

The Aeneid

Translated by W F Jackson Knight

In this prose translation, W F Jackson Knight discusses *The Aeneid*'s impact on Western civilization and provides a list of variations from the Oxford text.

440518 368pp £5.99

The Eclogues

Translated with an introduction by Guy Lee

Written between 42 and 37 BC, ten pastoral poems believed to be the first authentic work by Virgil are presented with the original Latin on the left-hand page and the translation on the right.

44419X 144pp £6.99

The Georgics

Translated and with an introduction by L P Wilkinson

A eulogy to Italy as the temperate land of perpetual spring, and a celebration of the values of rustic piety, *The Georgics* is probably the supreme achievement of Latin poetry.

444149 160pp £6.99

Virgil in English

Edited with an introduction by K W Grandsen

For T S Eliot, Virgil was not merely one of the great masters but 'our classic, the classic of all Europe'. Perhaps no other writer has generated a longer and larger tradition of commentary, translation and imitation. This selection consists largely of straight translations, along with a number of pieces illustrating Virgil's influence; celebrated episodes like the death of Dido, and Aeneas's descent into the underworld, appear in several different versions.

423869 384pp £8.99

COLLECTIONS

LATIN LITERATURE

AN ANTHOLOGY

Edited with an introduction by
Michael Grant

The translators in this anthology range from Sir Philip Sidney and Alexander Pope to contemporaries, and the text begins with Plautus (200 BC) and ends with St Augustine (AD 400). These selections show how Latin literature developed from Hellenistic imitations to works of true originality in thought and style.

443894 464pp £9.99

LIVES OF THE LATER CAESARS

Translated with an introduction by
Anthony Birley

Covering the emperors from Hadrian to Heliogabalus (AD 117–222), this edition contains the only true sequel to Suetonius's *The Twelve Caesars.*

443088 336pp £8.99

ROMAN POETS OF THE EARLY EMPIRE

Edited with an introduction by John Sullivan and Anthony Boyle

In this stimulating anthology, master poets of the so-called Silver Age – starting with Ovid, the first 'post-classical' poet after his exile in AD 8, including Seneca, Petronius, Lucan, Statius and others, and ending with the Emperor Hadrian (76–138), author of a celebrated verse addressed to his soul – demonstrate their magnificent literary achievements.

445447 480pp £9.99

INDEX

Courtesy of Bridgeman Art Library

A

B

C

D

E

N

O

PENGUIN CLASSICS

SIMPLY THE GREATEST RANGE OF LITERATURE IN THE WORLD

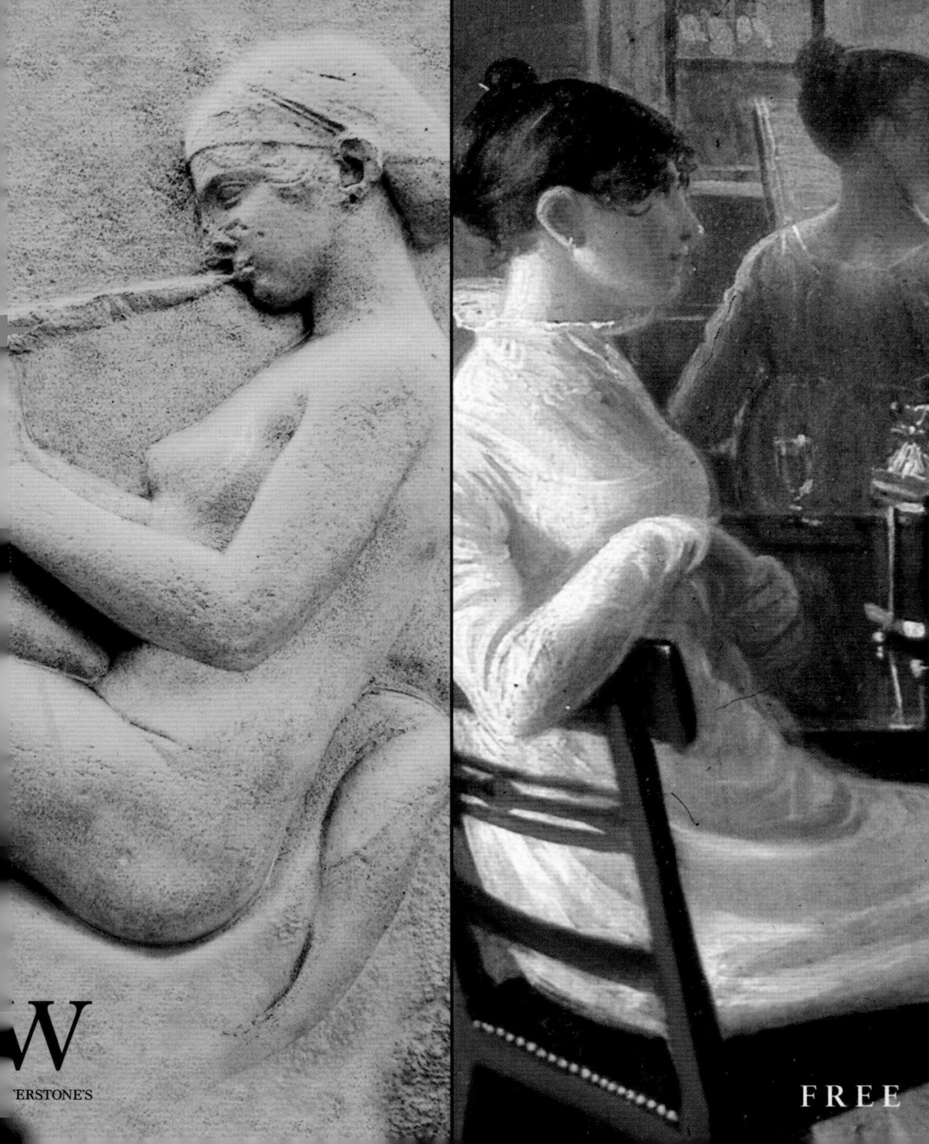

T

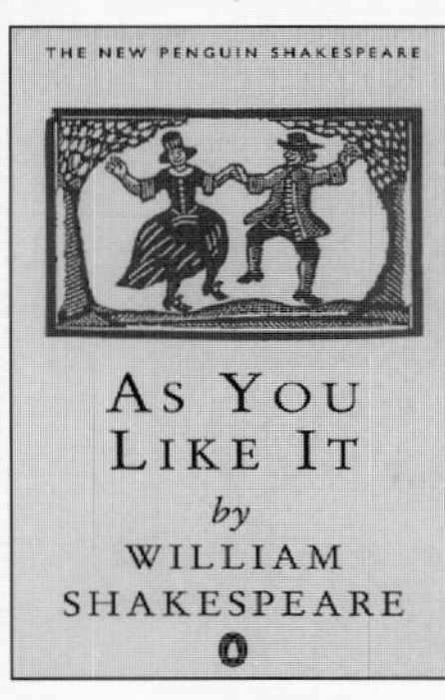

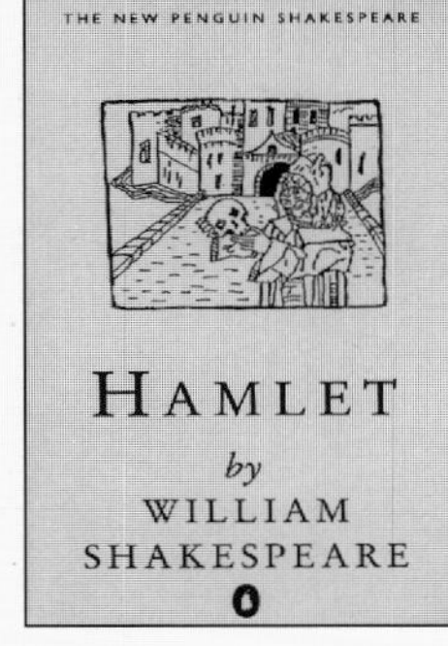

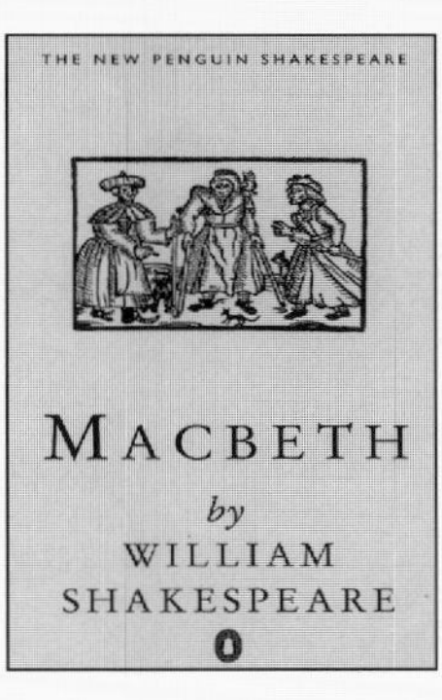

THE NEW PENGUIN SHAKESPEARE

General Editors: T J B Spencer and Stanley Wells

USED AND RECOMMENDED BY THE ROYAL SHAKESPEARE COMPANY

707204	All's Well That Ends Well	£3.99
70731X	Antony and Cleopatra	£3.99
70714X	As You Like It	£2.99
707255	Comedy of Errors	£3.99
707034	Coriolanus	£3.99
707344	Hamlet	£2.99
707182	Henry IV, Part One	£3.99
70728X	Henry IV, Part Two	£3.99
707085	Henry V	£3.99
707352	Henry VI, Part One	£5.50
707360	Henry VI, Part Two	£4.99
707379	Henry VI, Part Three	£5.99
707220	Henry VIII	£5.99
707042	Julius Caesar	£3.50
707271	King John	£4.99
707247	King Lear	£3.50
707387	Love's Labour's Lost	£3.99
707050	Macbeth	£3.50
707158	Measure for Measure	£3.50
707069	Merchant of Venice	£3.99
707263	Merry Wives of Windsor	£4.99
707026	Midsummer Night's Dream	£3.50
707093	Much Ado About Nothing	£3.50
707077	Othello	£2.99
707298	Pericles	£4.99
707190	Richard II	£2.99
707123	Richard III	£3.50
707018	Romeo and Juliet	£3.50
707328	The Sonnets/Lover's Complaint	£6.99
707107	Taming of the Shrew	£3.99
707131	The Tempest	£3.50
707212	Timon of Athens	£5.99
707417	Troilus and Cressida	£3.99
707115	Twelfth Night	£3.50
707174	Two Gentlemen of Verona	£5.99
707301	Two Noble Kinsmen	£5.99
707166	Winter's Tale	£3.50
150080	Portable Shakespeare	£9.99

EACH VOLUME HAS BEEN METICULOUSLY EDITED BY A LEADING SHAKESPEARIAN AUTHORITY

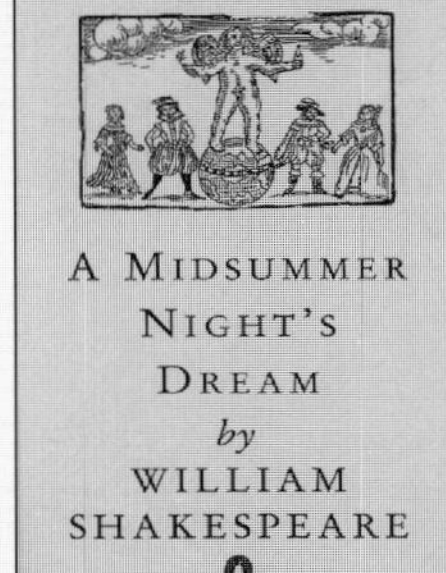

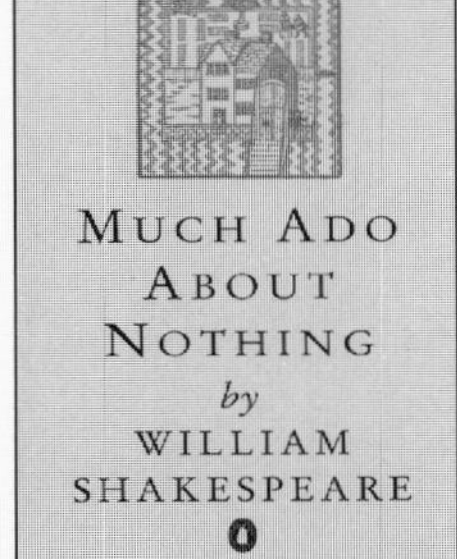

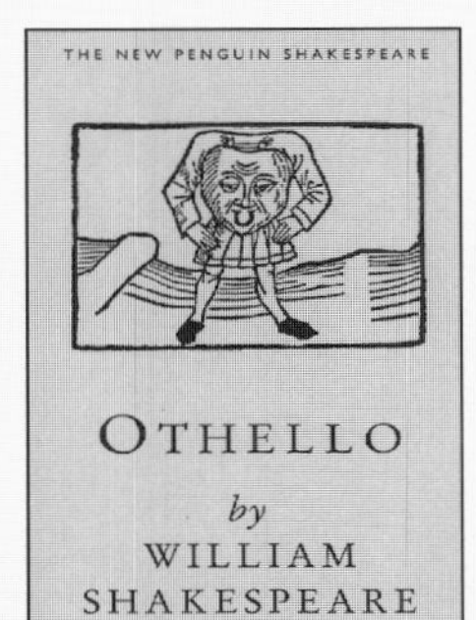

A UNIQUE AND ORIGINAL LIST WHICH REFLECTS THE BRILLIANCE AND DIVERSITY OF THE VERY BEST WRITING OF OUR ERA.

GABRIEL GARCÍA MÁRQUEZ
One Hundred Years of Solitude
VLADIMIR NABOKOV
A Russian Beauty and Other Stories
RALPH ELLISON
Flying Home
and Other Stories

THE FEAST

A mouth-watering celebration of eating, drinking and indulgence drawn entirely from the Penguin Classics and Twentieth-Century Classics.

437274 208pp £2.99

NEW NOVEMBER 98

NIGHT THOUGHTS

'I saw Eternity the other night
Like a great Ring of pure and endless light,
All calm as it was bright ...'

Drawn entirely from Penguin Classics, some of it famous, some obscure, ecstatic or despairing, morose or satirical, *Night Thoughts* is both an insomniac's companion and a celebration of some of the greatest writing in English.

436952 208pp £2.99

SEA LONGING

Behold, the sea itself,
And on its limitless, heaving breast, the ships
Panting and snorting like a mad battle steed
that has lost its rider,
the masterless ocean overruns the globe.

From Shakespeare, Marvell and Donne to Melville, Poe and Conrad, *Sea Longing* charts this great theme through both time and space. Drawn entirely from Penguin Classics and Twentieth-Century Classics, *Sea Longing* celebrates the amazing literary richness of this relationship.

436987 240pp £2.99